FOREWORD

My introduction to John Ramsbottom came almost ? O.S. Nock's *Premier Line* books and E.L. Ahrons outstanding and almost contemporary six part work on Victorian locomotives, so I learnt about his six designs and standardisation policies. I picked up information about some of his inventions, a type of safety valve and water troughs, almost by osmosis but it wasn't until this century that I realised Ramsbottom was a son of the 'border town' of Todmorden. This brought me into contact with the author of this publication who has produced a wonderful biography born of diligent research and which removes any ignorance of the abilities of John Ramsbottom which might remain.

Ramsbottom was one of the second wave of Victorian engineers making sure that the new machines were reliable as well as exciting. Through organisational zeal and forward thinking, Ramsbottom took standardisation to an unprecedented level; he made the workshops at Crewe the envy of all other engineer-managers and a byword for self-sufficiency. He invented devices which steam locomotives and other engines still use (and need) to this day.

His contribution to the development of the London & North Western Railway was huge and successive engineers built on Ramsbottom's firm foundations but, after 29 years with that Company, he chose to 'retire' at the then early age of 57, returning to railway affairs 12 years later in 1883 with the Lancashire & Yorkshire Railway where his effect was equally important.

Once again it was the organisation and management of locomotive works which interested him and he left his second Company with the greatest of legacies – the most modern, forward thinking railway works in Great Britain. He was the facilitator who made certain that his former pupil, John Aspinall, was appointed to enhance the L. & Y., though Ramsbottom never saw the whole contribution his champion made. Twentieth century locomotive engineers trained there who went on to dominate design policy were all influenced directly by him.

The adjectives applicable to John Ramsbottom are many but I will settle for 'outstanding' as study of this biography will display.

Noel Coates, Burnley, April 2008

**UNITS OF MEASURE: Imperial units are used throughout this book.
Metric equivalents are: 1 inch (in) = 25.4mm, 12 inches = 1 foot (ft);
14.5 pounds per square inch (p.s.i.) = 1 bar;
16 ounces (oz) = 1 pound (lb), 2.2 lbs = 1 kilogram.**

Opposite: **This 1816 map of Todmorden, surveyed by William Robinson, shows the canal, by then almost twenty years old, and the sparsely populated town strung out along the banks of the River Calder.** *Roger Birch.*

Front Cover: **This portrait of John Ramsbottom is by the artist William Percy (1820-1903) and was painted in Ramsbottom's home about 1880.**
Author's Collection, from an original in the National Railway Museum.

Rear Cover: **The only preserved Ramsbottom standard gauge engine is this L.N.W.R. 0-4-0 tank in the National Collection at Shildon.** *Noel Coates.*

Published by
The **Lancashire & Yorkshire Railway** *Society*

Founded 1950   Registered Charity No. 1098492

www.lyrs.org.uk

Our Purpose

The Lancashire & Yorkshire Railway Society is devoted to the dissemination of information about the Lancashire & Yorkshire Railway throughout its 75 years of existence and beyond. The Society has established an ongoing permanent record of its findings through its publications, which are widely available from the website, exhibition stands and specialist booksellers. It works closely with the National Railway Museum, the Greater Manchester County Record Office and other relevant bodies to ensure that original artifacts, records and other materials are professionally preserved and made accessible to all.

Membership Officer

Ken Carter, 11 Waveney Close, Arnold, Nottingham NG5 6QH
t: 0115 967 3485 e: membership@lyrs.org.uk

Publication Sales Officer

Alex Hodson, The L&YR Society, PO Box 110, Launceston PL15 9ZN
t: 01566 776463..e: sales@lyrs.org.uk

Copyright © 2007 Robin Pennie and *The* **L&YR** *Society*

Edited, designed and typeset by Roger Mellor

IT Adviser Martyn J. Wilkins

Printed in Baskerville typeface
Designed in 1757 by John Baskerville (1707-1775)

Published in association with
The London & North Western Railway Society
www.lnwrs.org.uk
Membership Secretary
Rev. B. Harris, 16 Westminster Green, Handbridge, Chester CH4 7LE

ACKNOWLEDGEMENTS

I would like to thank the many people have assisted me with information and technical advice in the writing of this book.

Those deserving special recognition are:-
Rev. John Bearpark; Vicar of Bentham, Mrs. Dorothy Clarkson, formerly the Registrar for Todmorden; Dr.Michael Grieve; Mr.D.Gunning, Todmorden Fine Art; Mr Malcolm Haywood; Mr. Michael Kenyon; Mr. Harry Kershaw; The late Denis O'Neill;   Mr.J.D.Storah, of Storah Architecture, for assistance in establishing the site of the Steam Factory; The late Rodney Weaver.

The Northern Mill Engine Society; Todmorden Antiquarian Society, The London & North Western Railway Society; The South Eastern & Chatham Railway Society; The Caledonian Railway Association.

Staff at the following institutions have also greatly helped:-
Barnsley Central Library; Bolton Central Library; Calderdale M.B.C.; Guardian Insurance; The Institution of Mechanical Engineers; Leeds City Council, Patent Information Unit; Manchester Central Library; Manchester Museum of Science and Industry; The Mitchell Library, Glasgow; The National Archives; The National Railway Museum; The University of Manchester.

Special thanks are also due to Roger Mellor for his skill, enthusiasm, and patience in creating this book and, most importantly, to my wife, Sarah, whose support and advice have been invaluable over more than a dozen years.

JOHN RAMSBOTTOM
A Victorian Engineering Giant

ROBIN PENNIE

CONTENTS

INTRODUCTION

Todmorden is a small market town in the Pennines on the Lancashire - Yorkshire border. Its industrial history is largely one of cotton manufacturing - an industry which, in its heyday a hundred years ago, supported a population of over 25,000, but which has now disappeared after a bare two hundred years.

John Ramsbottom started his life at the beginning of the "Age of Cotton" and it was the cotton industry that formed his early engineering development. It is said that he was even born in a room that resonated with the engine of his father's spinning mill next door.

From Todmorden the Steam Age took Ramsbottom into a world dominated, if not obsessed, by the development of railways. In his book The *Railway Engineers* O.S. Nock described Ramsbottom as one of the greatest locomotive engineers of the mid-Victorian period. Despite his fame and reputation when at the height of his powers, he is largely forgotten and has become little more than a footnote in other people's biographies. Crewe and Horwich have a Ramsbottom Street each, and in 2003 a wall plaque was erected in his memory at Todmorden station but, one hundred and ten years after his death, that is all. The aim of this book is to further a process that will give him the recognition that is his due.

EARLY DAYS IN TODMORDEN

To begin at the beginning - John Ramsbottom was born in Todmorden on 11 September 1814 at a house on the Rochdale Road, and was the second surviving son of Henry and Sarah Ramsbottom. In order to understand, however, what Todmorden was like at the time John Ramsbottom was born we need to go back to the late 1790s, some fifteen years earlier.

By the end of 1798 the Rochdale Canal was open through from Sowerby Bridge to Rochdale. One of the first people to realise the potential for development close to the canal in the Salford area of Todmorden was an earlier John Ramsbottom, a tailor in the town, and the grandfather of the engineer. He saw that the new canal would bring a reduction in freight transport costs, making it possible for manufacturers in Todmorden to compete with those close to Manchester. In 1799 he leased a plot of land for 999 years from the Crossley family, then the owners of the Old Hall estate and the Hall Ings. By 1804 this plot contained a dyehouse, a smithy, and five dwelling houses or cottages.

The development of the town as a whole is not relevant to the life of the engineer John Ramsbottom, except in two important respects. The first is the fact that his grandfather and father constructed the first steam powered cotton spinning mill in Todmorden, known as the "Steam Factory". According to an article in the *Todmorden Advertiser* in 1895 it had employed some 50 people. This venture must have been a considerable risk as tailor John Ramsbottom, and his son Henry, did not have an engineering background, though Henry must have received some training from the engine manufacturers at the very least. As the young Ramsbottom was a self-taught engineer, and never an apprentice to any trade, this factory and its engine are important not only because of them being the first in the town, but because they were where he developed his mechanical skills.

The second important respect is that the Salford area of Todmorden ("The Cradle of Todmorden Industries", as it has been called) was dominated for many years by the Ramsbottoms, the Chambers family, and the Holts, who as it turns out were all related by marriage. Not only would young Ramsbottom have been familiar with his grandfather's tailoring, and his father's cotton spinning businesses, but also with the Chambers' printing, and cloth dyeing, and the Holts' sawmill business at the nearby woodyard. The proximity of this area to the canal meant that it was the ideal place for industry to develop in Todmorden.

The relationship between the Chambers family, the Ramsbottoms, and the Holts is made clear in the will of Jonas Chambers the printer and bookbinder who died in 1829. As far as is known Henry Ramsbottom's wife Sarah, and Jonas Chambers' wife Hannah were two Holt sisters, making John Ramsbottom and Richard Chambers, the founder of the *Todmorden Advertiser*, full first cousins.

No previously published work on the history of Todmorden gives a date for the building of the Steam Factory, but the date for this can be definitely established, as can its location. The evidence is contained in title deeds belonging to Calderdale Metropolitan Borough Council. This involves a departure from what is generally held to have been the location for the Steam Factory.

The Steam Factory was located on land, now unfortunately under tarmac, adjacent to the industrial units on Salford Way. This is the only site in the area where the sizes of plots of land bought and leased at various times can be seen to fit both the Robinson survey of 1816 and the Ordnance Survey of 1848. It is also the only site where there is any indication of a mill chimney, an essential feature for a factory burning around a ton of coal a day.

As to the date of its construction, this can be put at late 1804 to early 1805. The reason that such a precise date is possible is because the Ramsbottoms were short of money after finishing the construction of the factory, and took out a mortgage in April 1805 to keep them going. This document, which still exists, contains a stipulation that the newly completed factory should be insured against fire for £500 with a "reputable company". It is clear from information supplied by Guardian Insurance that cotton spinning was considered a high risk activity, with highly loaded premiums.

As the Rochdale Canal was completed through to Manchester in December 1804 it is very likely that the major components for the new engine, and the spinning machinery, would have been brought to the site by canal boat. One "Rochdale flat", 72 feet long by 14 feet wide, would have been easily able to carry a load equal to that of many horse-drawn waggons, and the load would have suffered much less damage in consequence.

The Steam Factory is listed in the Crompton Spindle Survey of 1811 as "Todmorden Steam" with 2,592 mule spindles (12 x 18 dozen), and 480 throstle spindles (4 x 120), 3,072 in total. At this time the only larger spinning mills in the town were Ridgefoot Mill ("Todmorden Water" in Crompton) with 3,300 spindles and Waterside Mill with 3,144. All of these figures are dwarfed, however, by the mills in the Preston area, several of which had 15,000 to 20,000 spindles.

There was a major development at the factory in early 1824, which is revealed by another mortgage. This document refers to the factory being 9 yards in depth and 10 yards in length and having been recently increased from three storeys to four. While there had been small improvements in power transmission to reduce frictional losses in the twenty years since the Steam Factory was built, bevel gears and shafting were universally used till the 1850s. The Northern Mill Engine Society has advised that the extra spindles, or other power operated equipment, would have required extra power, most likely from a new, higher pressure, boiler operating at around

20-30 pounds per square inch (p.s.i) rather than the 10 p.s.i. that was normal in 1805.

The nearest contemporary account to this rebuilding of the factory is in Baines' 1825 *History, Directory, and Gazetteer, of the County Palatine of Lancaster.* In its introductory section on Todmorden it says that "in addition to the numerous water mills, there are in the town and neighbourhood no fewer than twelve steam engines, of the aggregate power of about one hundred and fifty horses." (This excludes one of "sixty horses power" that was about to be constructed by the Fielden Bros. at Waterside Mill.)

At this point it is necessary to explain that the power of early steam engines was often quoted in terms of "nominal horse power", "horses power", and even "shire horse power", rather than James Watt's figure of horse power. This creates some difficulties in assessing the power of an engine built two hundred years ago, and long since scrapped.

What is known of Ramsbottom at this time? Information is sketchy, because no family papers have survived. The most reliable information available about his upbringing is to be found in his obituary in the proceedings of the Institution of Mechanical Engineers.

According to this obituary, "his education was that of a remote village, where after a short time spent in a dame's school he went to four schoolmasters in succession, then to a Baptist minister, then to a colleague of the latter, who taught him as far as simple equations, leaving him to show afterwards, like many other self-educated men, that the true university was his own mind and power of thought."

It is not now possible to know which dame school Ramsbottom went to or who "the four schoolmasters in succession" were, but it is more than likely that his uncle Joseph Chambers, who died in 1835 and was classed as a schoolmaster when his estate was proved, would have played some part in his education, either as one of his teachers, or at least as an adviser on his education. One of the Baptist ministers concerned is likely to have been the Rev. George Dean, who is listed in Baines, as running an academy in the Todmorden district of Lineholme.

As only about 25% of children in Todmorden received any formal education in the 1830s, it is clear that Henry Ramsbottom, known to be a founder member of the Unitarian Church in the town, was taking great pains to give his son the best education available locally, contrary to the somewhat derogatory tone of the obituary notice.

In *The Locomotive Engineers*, O.S. Nock says "one revels in the story of him as a lad of sixteen journeying from Todmorden into Manchester to see the opening of the Liverpool and Manchester Railway." It is worth noting that the official opening was on Wednesday 15 September 1830, just four days after Ramsbottom's 16th birthday. As there is currently no supporting evidence for this story, Nock would appear to have had access to family papers that have now been destroyed or are in a private collection. Assuming that the story is true, then this may well have been a turning point in Ramsbottom's life - the day he realised that the steam engine could be used for transport in ways that had hitherto only been dreamed of.

EARLY SKILLS

It is clear that Ramsbottom's formal education was at least adequate to his needs then and later. It is also clear that he must have had a considerable native mechanical talent in view of the machines he constructed while working at his father's factory. After being "given a six inch lathe by his father, he constructed various models of steam engines, including a beam engine with condenser, an oscillating engine, Hero's reaction engine, a water raising engine, and a small locomotive engine to run upon a table or upon the floor." It is likely that most of these projects were accomplished while Ramsbottom was in his late teens.

It is also clear that he was an "active and enthusiastic" member of the first Mechanics Institute in the town, and of its successor, the "Athenaeum Club". He is said to have had "quick

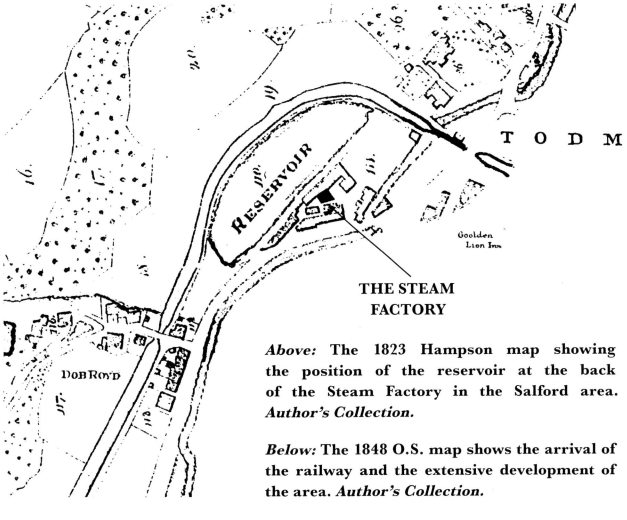

THE STEAM FACTORY

Above: The 1823 Hampson map showing the position of the reservoir at the back of the Steam Factory in the Salford area. *Author's Collection.*

Below: The 1848 O.S. map shows the arrival of the railway and the extensive development of the area. *Author's Collection.*

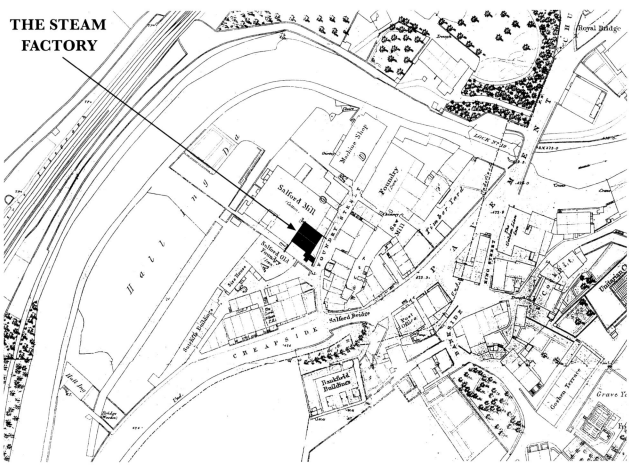

THE STEAM FACTORY

literary perception, and an appreciation of whatever was graceful and intellectual". It was to benefit the funds of the "Athenaeum Club" that the locomotive mentioned above was displayed "traversing a circular line of rails on a platform." Unfortunately there were no newspapers published in the town at the time, so there are no reports of this event.

Returning to the Institution of Mechanical Engineers obituary we find that "later he made a stationary 'table' engine, with upright 5-inch cylinder and 18-inch stroke, and an overhead crosshead with side-rods down to a crankshaft underneath the table; it was worked with steam of the then high pressure of 50 p.s.i, of which the villagers took notice that it looked rather blue as it escaped from the safety valve."

Again we find that "for a friend who was a confectioner he made an engine with 4-inch cylinder and 12-inch stroke." If it was used in Todmorden, it must have been near one of the local streams in order to provide water for the boiler and jet condenser. It would be interesting to have information about these engines. Where were they installed, how successful were they, and how long did they last?

Ramsbottom's first patent, Nº 6644, was taken out in 1834 in conjunction with Richard Holt of Todmorden, ironfounder, and very probably his uncle. At this time he was only 19 and unable to take out a patent in his own name. It is likely that Richard Holt was not only providing the name of an adult for legal reasons, but also providing some or all of the money. The subject of this patent included the famous "Weft-Fork". The "Fork" part of its name came from the fact that it looked like a carving fork with long prongs. Its function on power looms was as an automatic stop device that came into action as soon as it detected the weft thread was broken, or needed replacing because it had run out.

Curiously the Weft-Fork was a minor part of the patent, the major part of the text being devoted to a vertical axis double loom capable of weaving two pieces of cloth at once. While such looms may have been made in limited numbers in the nineteenth century, their manufacture

did not become commonplace. The Weft-Fork became much more important very quickly, because it could be applied to power looms of all types. According to the *Todmorden Advertiser's* obituary:- "By this invention alone Mr. Ramsbottom became a benefactor to the weaver class of workers in an incalculable degree."

ENGINE REBUILDING AND NEW IDEAS

The middle 1830s were a boom period when money was available for the rebuilding of the engine at the Steam Factory. As there are no Ramsbottom mortgages for this period it is possible that the rebuilding work was financed by the Ramsbottoms alone, but given their financial history it seems more likely that the costs were shared with the Chambers Brothers who had the adjacent factory and probably shared the power produced. In the Institution of Mechanical Engineers obituary we find the following:- "Of more importance was the reconstruction and erection of the engine in his father's mill, including a larger cylinder of 18 inches diameter and four feet stroke, a new beam, connecting-rod, air-pump, and condenser, the last two being purchased from Messrs. Peel, Williams, and Peel, Soho Iron Works, Manchester; he also fitted up new side pipes with slide-valves and a new parallel-motion."

It is not clear from the list of parts purchased if the new cylinder was larger in diameter or stroke, or both. On the basis of the information provided, it can only have been larger in diameter, for the following reasons. The beam of a beam engine needs to have roughly equal arms rocking round a central pivot on top of a pillar. Any change in the piston stroke requires at the very least a new crankshaft to cope with the increase in stroke, because the piston stroke and the crankpin circle have to be in the same ratio as the two arms of the beam, and it is not possible to increase the movement of only one of them. Fitting a new crankshaft to an existing flywheel would have involved an even bigger reconstruction of the engine than is recorded.

The lack of any mention of a new crankshaft means it can be safely inferred that the stroke was unchanged.

No mention is made of a new boiler being fitted during the rebuilding, though a more powerful engine would be likely to need more steam, even allowing for an increase in efficiency. As indicated earlier, the boiler is likely to have been renewed in the 1820s and would have had sufficient capacity to supply the new larger cylinder.

Obviously the rebuilding of the engine at the Steam Factory gave Ramsbottom the experience of dealing with two or more contractors, which must have been valuable in itself. How far the detailed redesigning of the engine was his own work is something that can no longer be established. Though he was a brilliant natural mechanic, it is not clear whether he gave the contractors a specification to meet, sketches of what he wanted, or complete detailed plans. Whichever way it happened, this was a considerable organisational achievement for someone of no more than 21.

At about the same time that the engine for the Steam Factory was being rebuilt, the building was fitted with gas lighting, again organised by Ramsbottom. The nearest gasworks was that of the Fielden Brothers, at Waterside Mill, who supplied several businesses and factories in the locality on a commercial basis. No visible trace survives of the gas main over or under the nearby Walsden Water used to supply the works.

Not all this practical work involved steam engines of various sorts. He also schemed, made, and successfully worked an automatic machine for the manufacture of cut nails. (This involves creating nails with integral heads from strips of metal, rather than each nail being crafted individually by hand from two separate pieces of metal.)

The range of Ramsbottom's interests can be gauged from the fact that, in addition to the diverse machinery already described, he developed a printing machine, presumably taking advice from his printer uncle Jonas Chambers. Its development was later dropped.

His second patent, like his first, was entirely to do with textile machinery. Patent N° 6975 of 1836 is for the roving, spinning and doubling of cotton (and other fibres) using modifications of the traditional throstle spinning frame. Presumably there must have been experiments at the Steam Factory to develop the idea to the point where it could be patented. How successful Ramsbottom was in having this process widely adopted is not known.

Returning to the Ramsbottom family, it becomes clear that they were not supporters of the Church of England because Henry and Sarah Ramsbottom's family were not baptised until 26 June 1837, only five days before the start of the compulsory registration of births, marriages, and deaths. It appears that the Church of England, at the time, successfully misled many people into believing that their future marriage or death could not be registered when the new secular system of registration came into operation unless they had first been baptised. No doubt the fees were very welcome, particularly as on the same day five Ramsbottoms and ten Holts were baptised, including two of Ramsbottom's aunts (see Appendix Seven). The ages of those baptised ranged from his youngest sister Ann who was 17, through Ramsbottom himself who was 23, to the older of his two aunts who was 42!

The year 1839 saw the start of a serious general recession which lasted for several years. With two patents under his belt Ramsbottom may well have felt that Todmorden had little left to offer him. He was 24, ambitious, and probably saw that his father's business would not survive long. If it was absorbed by that of his Chambers uncles next door, then he would be in an inferior position to the one he had running the Steam Factory for his father. He also had, as has been shown, a well developed interest in engineering, not just the textile industry.

Richard Roberts now enters the scene. Roberts was a partner in Sharp, Roberts, and Co. in Manchester, and had made a name for himself by inventing many types of machines, particularly the self-acting mule in 1825. According to Dr. Andrew Ure's *Dictionary of Arts, Manufactures and Mines*, published in 1839, there were "probably . . . upwards of half a million spindles of Messrs. Sharp, Roberts, and Co's construction at work in the United Kingdom, and giving great satisfaction to their possessors."

Somebody with Roberts' record as an inventor would certainly have kept a look out for new patents that the firm could manufacture, and he may well have spotted the potential of Ramsbottom's patents.

Up until now the possibility of there being a connection between John Ramsbottom and Richard Roberts has been ignored, but the evidence is that it was important, and was one of the reasons for him leaving Todmorden and starting a new life with Sharp, Roberts, and Co. in 1839. Putting it in modern terms, he may well have been head-hunted by Roberts. From the *Todmorden Advertiser's* obituary it is clear that

he was "greatly endeared" to the Roberts family, and that "in the early part of his career Mr. Richd. Roberts was an occasional visitor to Todmorden with him". Jumping forward twenty-five years, it is also worth noting that, according to the biographical note published by the Manchester Association of Engineers, Ramsbottom was one of the pall-bearers at Roberts' funeral in 1864 in London.

When Ramsbottom left Todmorden in the Spring of 1839 for Manchester he took with him references from local manufacturers. Fortunately these survive at the National Archives. What is of particular interest is the reference from James Taylor of Todmorden Hall which says that Ramsbottom's "attention has for many years past been more particularly devoted to matters connected with the Steam Engine".

Below: The house nearest the camera on what is now Rochdale Road, Todmorden, is where John Ramsbottom is thought to have been born. *Roger Birch 1970.*

MANCHESTER YEARS 1839-1857

Ramsbottom appears to have been employed from the outset in the locomotive department of Sharp, Roberts, and Co. "Thanks to the practical experience he had acquired at home", as the Institution of Mechanical Engineers obituary puts it, "he at once obtained employment and pay, without preliminary apprenticeship; and here he first gained practical knowledge and experience of the construction of locomotives." It is also interesting to note from the obituary in the *Todmorden Advertiser* that one of the main reasons for his choosing to be a locomotive engineer "was from consideration for the miserable horses which he often saw on the roads drawing heavy loads".

As some readers will have vivid memories of the Beeching era with its heavy cuts in the railway network, it is difficult to think oneself into the 1830s when the network was growing, and rapidly. In 1836 there were only 400 miles of public railways in Britain, but only four years later in 1840 there were 1,500 miles. As the number of miles of railway increased, so did the need for new locomotives to haul trains along the tracks.

Sharp, Roberts, and Co. were already established locomotive builders by the time that Ramsbottom joined them, and during the year 1839 to 1840 alone they received orders from the following British railways:- Manchester and Birmingham; Glasgow, Paisley and Greenock; London and Brighton; Great Western; Bristol

Above: **The Sharp, Roberts, and Co. standard 2-2-2 tender engine was in production for twenty years from 1837 and Ramsbottom would have been involved in the building and commissioning of many of the type. One of many users was the Manchester & Leeds Railway which became the L.&Y.R. in 1847.** *Source unknown.*

and Exeter; and Manchester and Leeds. Orders from European railways came from the Netherlands Government; Grand Duchy of Baden; Magdeburg and Leipzig; and the Brunswick Government. These are all orders that Ramsbottom would have come across in the works, and there has to be a strong possibility that he worked on the engine *Todmorden* which was one of six ordered by the Manchester and Leeds Railway in 1840.

The connection that Sharp, Roberts, and Co. established with German railways must have been assisted by the fact that the head of their locomotive department was Charles Frederick Beyer, a native of Saxony and only a year older than Ramsbottom. Soon after arriving in Manchester the two became friends, and the friendship lasted until Beyer's death many years later in 1876.

The locomotives that Sharp, Roberts, and Co. produced were to a limited number of designs. One of the most successful was a single-wheeler 2-2-2 tender engine which was in production, with modifications, from 1837 to 1857. Up until 1852 the Chief Draughtsman was Charles Beyer. Because very few railways at that time were building their own locomotives, Beyer therefore had considerable influence on designs of the period.

The three years that Ramsbottom spent with Sharp, Roberts, and Co. were a pivotal period in his life. When he arrived in Manchester he was an unknown man from Todmorden: three years later he was taken on by the Manchester and Birmingham Rly., at the age of 27, as Superintendent of Locomotives at their works in Longsight.

All previously published biographical information states that Ramsbottom was given the job at Longsight purely on the strength of Beyer's recommendation, but it does appear that he had to apply for the post, however much his application was a foregone conclusion. The letter was addressed to Captain Edward John Cleather, Manager of the Manchester and Birmingham Railway Company's London Road Station at his office in Piccadilly, Manchester. It reads as follows:-

Manchester, May 16th/42

Sir,

Having been given to understand through the medium of Messrs. Sharp Roberts & Co. of this town that the Manchester & Birmingham Rway Co. are wishfull to engage some one as Superintendant [sic] of Locomotives, and feeling assured that should I be fortunate enough to obtain the situation, I could perform satisfactorily the duties which attach to it, I now beg to offer myself as a candidate, most respectfully soliciting at the same time your kind interest & support in my behalf, - the sum of my qualifications is soon told, - if to a tolerable knowledge of decimal arithmetic a smattering of mensuration, geometry, mechanical science, and chemistry you add the experience which is naturally to be derived from an acquaintance of more than 15 yrs with the Steam Engine in its various forms, but more particularly from having witnessed, and assisted in the construction of nearly 150 Locomotive Engines of different kinds, you may form a tolerable idea of the grounds upon which I rest my hopes of success, - but enough: for tho to say nothing might appear like stupidity, - to say more might perhaps savour of egotism, both of which charges it is desirable to avoid. - perhaps it is sufficient to refer you to Messrs. Sharp Roberts & Co. whom I now have the pleasure to serve, I am no partizan, but resting my case upon its merits and your judgement

I beg to subscribe myself

Sir, Your most obedient Servt.

JOHN RAMSBOTTOM

It is only possible to speculate how far Beyer was protecting his own position at Sharp, Roberts, and Co. while benefitting his friend. Given their

Below: Sharp, Roberts, and Co. were originally located at the Globe Iron Works in Dickinson Street and, from 1839, also at the Atlas Iron Works in Great Bridgewater Street, as seen in this O.S. map of the area. Neither works had a rail connection but both were adjacent to the various branches of the Rochdale canal.

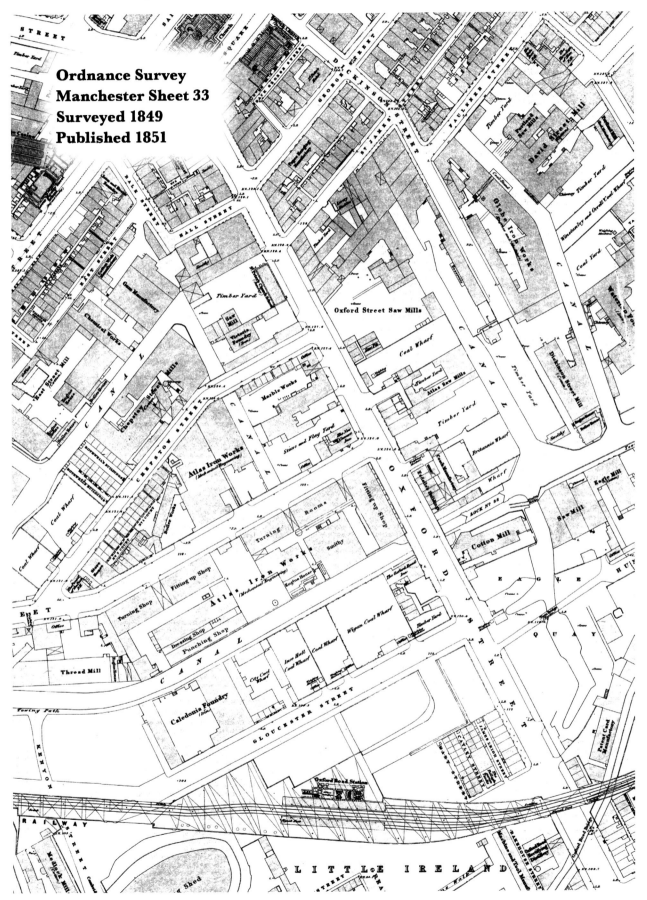

**Ordnance Survey
Manchester Sheet 33
Surveyed 1849
Published 1851**

abilities, ambition, and similar age, it might have been difficult to avoid a clash if they had both stayed in the same works.

As many of the locomotives owned by the Manchester and Birmingham Rly. had been supplied by Sharp, Roberts, and Co., Ramsbottom was ideally suited to look after them. This was obviously the view taken by the company, despite his lack of experience in railway working. The company was so satisfied with his work that after 18 months he was promoted to take charge of the locomotives and rolling stock at a salary of £170 per annum, when the mechanical and civil engineering departments were separated.

In 1846 the Manchester and Birmingham Railway had become one of the constituent parts of the London and North Western Railway, but this reorganisation did not change his position as the Locomotive Superintendent at Longsight. With increasing responsibility, his salary was substantially increased - from £300 to £500 in 1849 when the Manchester to Huddersfield line was opened, and to £850 in 1853.

After the formation of the L.N.W.R., Edward Watkin, who had been working on the Trent Valley Railway, became one of the assistants to the General Manager (Mark Huish), and Secretary of the Locomotive Committee. In this latter capacity he would have had regular dealings with Ramsbottom as the Committee was responsible for compiling statistics on the costs of fuel, maintenance, and repairs, for the whole locomotive fleet.

The rise in Ramsbottom's standing can be gauged from the fact that he was a founder member of the Institution of Mechanical Engineers in 1847 after only five years at Longsight. Preliminary discussions about such a body had started the previous year during locomotive trials on the Lickey incline, near Bromsgrove. Established engineers including Charles Beyer, Richard Peacock (later to form a partnership), and J.E. McConnell of the Southern Division of the London and North Western Rly. were strongly behind the formation of the Institution.

The third Ramsbottom patent dates from 1848, and was taken out in conjunction with William Baker of Edgbaston, near Birmingham. This Mr. Baker appears to be the William Baker listed as being at Longsight in a Manchester street directory of 1847. He was also a member of the Institution of Mechanical Engineers. The patent deals with two separate inventions - the use of ball bearings for railway turntables and as a thrust race to support shafts in factories, and also a new design of wheel for railway vehicles.

Ramsbottom's first paper to the Institution of Mechanical Engineers was read (in his absence) in 1849. It was entitled *On an Improved Locomotive Boiler*. After a few introductory remarks he stated his main position; that the power of a boiler is dependent on the quantity of steam it can produce in a given time, and hence the coal and air that it will burn. Because, in his view, many of the boilers then current had too little area through the tubes for them to steam freely, he proposed a new type of boiler with a steam and water drum above the normal boiler barrel, but connected to it by two large pipes. This would allow the ordinary barrel to be filled with tubes, giving a greater area through the tubes for the exhaust gases than before, leading to a greater flow of air through the grate, and more coal being burned. This boiler was similar to the Brotan type later developed in Hungary, but does not appear to have been used in Britain.

MARRIAGE AND NEW INVENTIONS

Here we need to take a look at Ramsbottom as a man with a private life, not just as an engineer. As a result of trawling through various 1851 census returns it can be stated categorically that on 30 March, the night of the Census, John Ramsbottom appears, not

Opposite page: **This first edition O.S. map shows the Carriage and Engine Depot at Longsight which was Ramsbottom's base from 1842 until 1857.** *Author's Collection.* **Inset: Belle Vue Place from the 1893 O.S. map. Mike Fitton Collection**

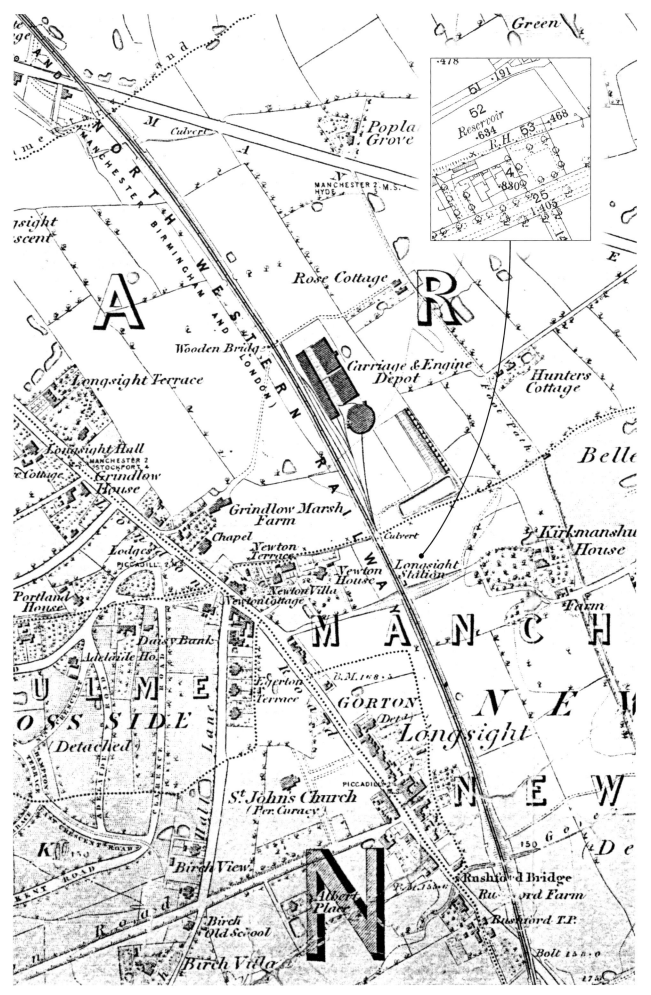

in the returns for Manchester where he might reasonably be expected to be, but staying at a house in Barnsley. One amusing point about this is that the Census enumerator was so unfamiliar with the concept of a Locomotive Superintendent, or misheard what he was told, that Ramsbottom is listed as a Primitive Methodist Superintendent!

Why Barnsley? Well the explanation appears to be that he was in Barnsley making arrangements for his forthcoming marriage, probably to hear the banns being read. The marriage took place on 29 April at St.George's Church, Barnsley, in front of several witnesses, including his prospective brother and sister-in-law, and his cousin from Todmorden, Richard Chambers.

The person he was marrying was Mary Peckett. She was the elder daughter of William Peckett, a Quaker linen-manufacturer there, who wore Quaker dress till the day he died in 1882, and was the last person in Barnsley to do so. He was also known to be a hard man in his dealings with his workers, evicting them from their cottages if they went on strike.

Above: **Ramsbottom in 1851.**
Science Museum

For Mary Peckett, marrying Ramsbottom was a serious step as the Quakers, at that time, excluded any member who married a non-Quaker. William Peckett did not sign the register at his daughter's wedding, and it is certainly possible that he so disapproved of her "marrying out" that he did not attend. As Ramsbottom was 36 and his wife about 34 at the time of the marriage, they were certainly "of full age" as the marriage certificate puts it.

The only connection with Barnsley that can be established is the Mechanics' Institute. As mentioned earlier, Ramsbottom was a strong supporter of the one in Todmorden, and it is probably no coincidence that his brother-in-law in Barnsley was a prominent member of the Barnsley Mechanics' Institute, in addition to being a local clock-maker. As there are no records of the Institute for 1849 and 1850 it is not known if he was invited across from Manchester for a lecture, but it is difficult to find another simple explanation for his initial introduction to Mary Peckett.

After their marriage the Ramsbottoms moved into one of a block of three new houses called Belle Vue Place (demolished in 1996). Their son William Henry Ramsbottom (named after both his grandfathers) was born here on 28 February 1852. From the Rating Rolls of the old Borough of Newton it becomes clear that these were owned not by the railway company but by the developer of the nearby Belle Vue Gardens.

Family life and professional advancement seem to have suited Ramsbottom as he took out no fewer than six patents between 1852 and 1857. The most famous of these is for the split piston ring, still in use after over 150 years on the majority of internal combustion engines. (It would be interesting to know how many other patents have had such a long life, and been so widely used.) In its day, the safety valve that he patented in 1855 was extremely important, and, because it could not be tampered with by anybody trying to raise the boiler pressure, it must have contributed an overall reduction in the number of explosions of both stationary and locomotive boilers.

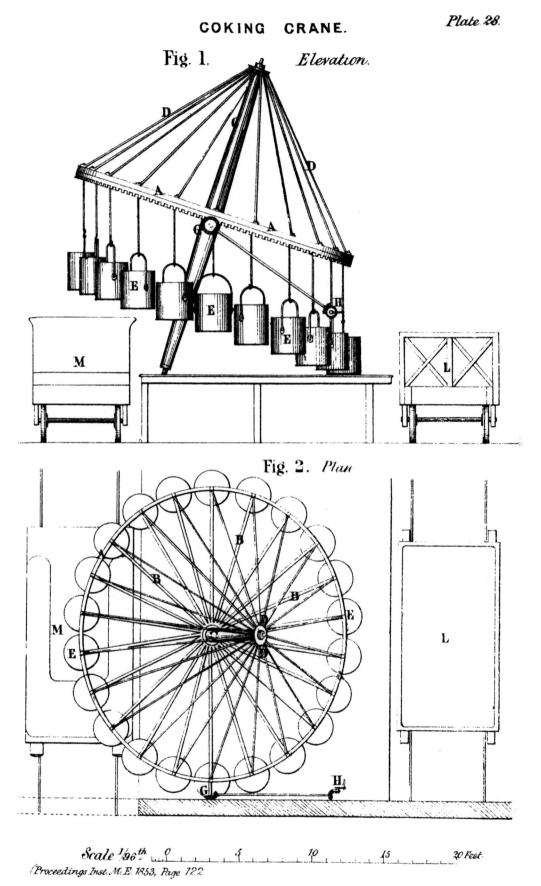

COKING CRANE.

Plate 28.

Fig. 1. Elevation.

Fig. 2. Plan

Scale 1/96th   0   5   10   15   20 Feet

(Proceedings Inst. M.E. 1853, Page 122)

Ramsbottom's second paper to the Institution of Mechanical Engineers, given in 1853, was the *Description of an Improved Coking Crane for Supplying Locomotive Tenders.* This device had been in use at Manchester London Road for the preceding two years and had allowed the number of men required to deliver coke to the locomotives to be reduced from four to two. *I. Mech. E.*

Ramsbottom was also a founder member of the Manchester Steam Users Association, along with other engineers including William Fairbairn and Joseph Whitworth, the latter being a personal friend. Inaugurated at a public meeting at the then Manchester Town Hall on 19 September 1854, the Association was very concerned about all aspects of boiler design and safety.

The L.N.W.R. was hampered from the outset by having locomotive works at Crewe, Longsight, and Wolverton, each with its own Locomotive Superintendent acting entirely independently. Even in 1847, the year after the Company came into existence, the Secretary, C.E.Stewart, had

The peace of the Longsight area was violently broken at 8.55 a.m. on 6th. March 1853 when the boiler of an elderly locomotive kept for pilot and shunting duties exploded inside the octagonal shed. The blast not only lifted the whole roof several inches but blew away one sixth of it entirely, besides shattering every pane of glass. Six men died. This shocking experience must have focused Ramsbottom's mind on the need to improve boiler safety and safety valves. *Author's Collection*

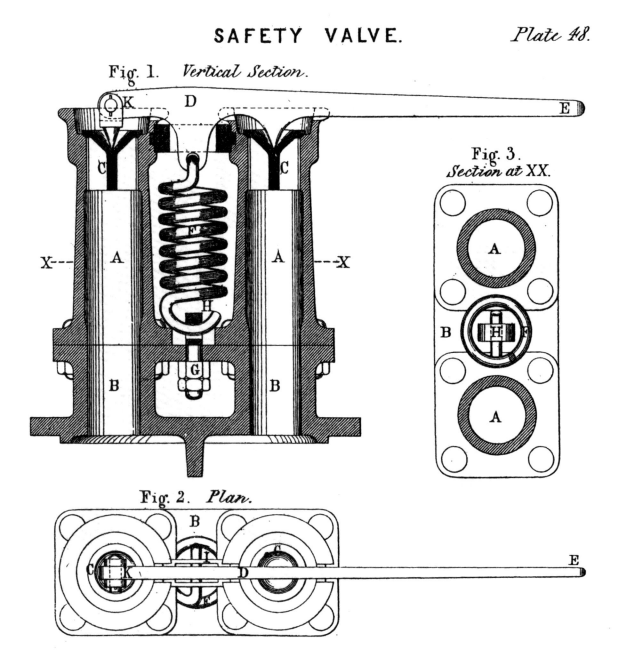

SAFETY VALVE. *Plate 48.*

Fig. 1. *Vertical Section.*

Fig. 3. *Section at XX.*

Fig. 2. *Plan.*

found that there were not only three accounting systems in use, but that at Crewe it was impossible to tell if the storekeeper's figures were accurate or not! Stewart's recommendations to improve matters were only dealt with half-heartedly.

Proposals for centralising the operations of all three Divisions had first been discussed in 1854-5, and the sub-committee reviewing the problem reported that the three works should be "consolidated under one general superintendent", but was not prepared to recommend an immediate change.

By December 1855 the Directors were becoming concerned about the quality of the locomotive building and repairing taking place at Crewe. The person they called on to advise them was Joseph Whitworth. As Whitworth had built up a reputation over the preceding twenty years for producing machine tools working to previously unheard of standards of accuracy, he was an obvious choice.

Whitworth reported back to the Directors in January 1856, pointing out that "there are some parts of your engines which are being continually worn out; the manufacture of these should be constantly in progress . . . (and) a stock kept . . . used for both the new and the repair of old engines."

Not only was the locomotive situation at Crewe unsatisfactory, but a rolling mill for wrought iron rails installed in 1853 was put under Ramsbottom's control, in addition to his duties at Longsight. Despite this substantial snub to his managerial skills, Francis Trevithick, the Locomotive Superintendent at Crewe, appears to have maintained friendly relations with Ramsbottom.

The three Locomotive Superintendents, Ramsbottom, Trevithick, and McConnell, were all consulted in 1855 by the sub-committee. It is possible that the knowledge that at least two of them would ultimately have to leave, or assume a subordinate position, may have influenced Ramsbottom to consider applying for the post of Locomotive Superintendent on the Eastern Counties Railway in 1856, even consulting the Chairman, the Marquis of Chandos about it.

A proposal to combine the Northern, and North Eastern Divisions, was brought forward in March 1856 when Richard Moon, one of the Directors, proposed that the two divisions should be combined under Ramsbottom, but this was not accepted. The proposal was finally agreed in March 1857, against the wishes of some of the Directors. As a result of the good opinion of him held by a few Directors, Trevithick was given a golden handshake of £3,000 on leaving, on account of his long service, and honourable personal character.

Ramsbottom had let it be known early in 1857 that, if he were chosen for the new combined Division, he would want a salary of £1,200 per annum, £200 more than the Board had in mind. Moon wrote to Chandos: "I hope you will not let £200 stand in the way . . . a trifle in salary is nothing to get the men you want . . . I look upon the labour for any one taking Crewe to put in order as herculean. It is the man, not the system, upon which we must depend. No system would work with Trevithick's weak hand, and I shall despair of any good to our concern if he is retained."

Moon was still concerned and wrote again to Chandos, on 5 May 1857. He repeated his

Above: **Trevithick (right) in the garden of Chester Place, with Webb, in 1875, two years before his death.**
Science Museum

views on Trevithick's weak management, and was very critical of the "laxity of the system" on the Northern Division. He concluded: "We shall never know what our engines are doing or what they might do if they are most scientifically disposed."

During this period of uncertainty, Ramsbottom was also having to cope with family concerns. His wife's health was deteriorating and, back in Todmorden, his sister Hannah had to give up the shop she had been running in order to spend more time looking after their mother.

Throughout the summer of that year, day to day work must have been considerably heavier than usual because of the exhibition of "Art Treasures of the United Kingdom" held at a special pavilion in the Old Trafford area of Manchester on what is now the Metrolink line to Altrincham. This even had its own station with 800ft. long platforms.

The Exhibition was a great success with over one million visits being made; the grand total was in fact 1,336,715. While the Exhibition made a profit of £304/14s/4d, the London and North Western Railway made a profit of £50,000 from the increased number of passengers. Many of the visitors to Manchester, and most of those attending the exhibition, would have arrived and departed from London Road station on special trains, and all the locomotives for these trains would have required to be supplied with coke, water, and lubricating oil, at Longsight shed.

After securing the post at Crewe, largely due to Richard Moon's recognition of his outstanding ability, Ramsbottom must have been looking forward to the time when he had control of the newly enlarged Northern Division, and was able to reorganise the works and the locomotives to meet the demands of the traffic.

Below: Stokers and Pokers published in 1849 casts some light on this Pass, as it includes a copy of the L.N.W.R. Rules and Regulations. In Section V (Regulations for Guards), number 25 states:- "Servants and others connected with the Railway (Directors excepted) are required to book and pay their fare the same as other Passengers, except the following Officers, who travel free, and have the power to grant Passes to individuals proceeding *on the Company's business only*". For the Locomotive Department the named officers are Mr. McConnell, Mr. Trevithick, and "Mr. Ramsbottom .. Man. and Bir. Section."
Courtesy of National Railway Museum.

CREWE 1857-1871

TRAGEDY . . .

The best way to describe the first few weeks of Ramsbottom's tenure of office at Crewe is to quote from the opening of Dickens' *Tale of Two Cities* - "It was the best of times, it was the worst of times".

The reason for its being the best of times is obvious: the reason for its being the worst of times has not previously been published. Within days of his starting at Crewe on 1 August his wife died at their house in Longsight, at the age of only 41. According to the death certificate the cause was "venous congestion of the lungs". The best medical advice is that she had probably suffered from rheumatic fever when young, which would have left her with a defective and deteriorating heart valve. Ramsbottom was present at her death and it was he who informed the Registrar.

The *Todmorden Advertiser* for 8 August 1857 contains the following short paragraph:-

"SUDDEN DEATH. - We are sorry to have to record the death of Mrs. Ramsbottom, wife of Mr. John Ramsbottom Esqr., of Longsight, Manchester, and formerly of this town, which took place yesterday morning. She is deeply regretted by all who knew her."

Less than a month after his wife's death on 7 August, his mother, Sarah, died in Todmorden on 1 September. (The cause of death on this occasion is given as "natural decay".) As a matter of Todmorden interest, she was one of the last people to be buried in the St. Mary's graveyard, in the same plot as a son who had died in infancy in 1812.

Opposite page: **Ramsbottom completed the first of his 793 DX Goods class 0-6-0s in September 1858 and they came to account for over 40% of the locomotive stock. No. 1080, seen here on a passenger working, emerged from Crewe in 1863. The displacement lubricator oil vessel is visible on the front footplate.** *Ian Allan Library.*

. . . AND PROGRESS

Up until Ramsbottom's arrival at Crewe all locomotives were constructed on an individual craft basis, not on any sort of batch or mass production. One result of this was that for the first couple of years he had to spend a large part of his time improving works discipline, and insisting that parts for locomotives were manufactured as specified. Many drawings of the period 1857-58 contain the inscription "work to dimensions" or "dimensions must be worked to".

Improving standards was all part of a larger strategy to equip the London and North Western Railway with new locomotives that could be produced and repaired cheaply and quickly. The most notable example of a Ramsbottom design is the DX goods class. The first one was completed in September 1858, and the design was so successful that production continued for fifteen years, with only minor modifications being made. Including engines built for the Lancashire and Yorkshire Railway, the total of 943 remains the highest for any class of railway engine built in this country. Not one of them survives unfortunately, though the last of them was not scrapped until 1930.

By the end of his first year at Crewe, Ramsbottom must have been feeling a lot more optimistic about his private life because he married again on 12 April 1859 in Stockport parish church. This time his bride was Mary Anne Goodfellow, the daughter of Benjamin Goodfellow - a fellow member of the Institution of Mechanical Engineers, a mill-engine manufacturer in Hyde, and only a couple of years older than his new son-in-law.

Unlike his first marriage in 1851, there is no doubt about his father-in-law being at the wedding. Benjamin Goodfellow was the first person to sign the register. The other signatures relevant here are those of his cousin from Todmorden,

Richard Chambers, and Charles Frederick Beyer - his old colleague from Manchester.

The family rejoicing may have been somewhat muted because Ramsbottom's father, Henry, died in Todmorden on 13 April, the day after the wedding. It is only possible to speculate, but it seems likely that the date of the wedding was brought forward because of his father's ill health. Given the proprieties of the time it would have been necessary, if his father had died any earlier, to delay the wedding till after a suitable period of mourning had elapsed - six months at least. (For those interested, Henry Ramsbottom's headstone survives in the graveyard of Christ Church, Todmorden.)

The year 1860 saw the birth of their first child, John Goodfellow, and Ramsbottom's next two patents. The first of these was for the water-trough, the second for a displacement lubricator which could be applied to stationary engines, as well as locomotives.

The provisional patent specification for "Improvements in Supplying the Tenders or Tanks of Locomotives Engines with Water" had been applied for on 23 June, [see also Appendix Two - Patents, and Appendix Four - Habits of Thought] and was the culmination of many tests. On 17 October Ramsbottom wrote to the Marquis of Chandos, the Chairman of the Company, as follows:-

"I beg to inform you that a few experiments will be made near the Conway Station on Tuesday next the 23rd inst. on my proposed method of supplying Tenders with water whilst in motion.

A special train for the conveyance of the Directors will leave Crewe at 9.20 and Chester at 10.0 a.m. on that day, and will return to Crewe in time to catch the Scotch Express in the evening."

The Directors were concerned at this time about the size of locomotives being used on the railway and they instructed Ramsbottom to compile a report. This survives in the National Archives, and is reprinted as Appendix One.

By 1862 Richard Moon, now the Chairman of the Company, and members of the Board were becoming seriously dissatisfied with the separation of the Railway into a Northern and a Southern Division. After a bitter internal dispute Ramsbottom was appointed to the position of Locomotive Superintendent of the whole L.N.W.R. on 22 March, at a salary of £2,000 per annum, with effect from 1 April. Fortunately, the letter of thanks that he wrote to Richard Moon on his appointment survives in the National Archives and is reproduced opposite.

IN COMPLETE CONTROL

The period 1862 - 1871 saw John Ramsbottom at the zenith of his career and proved his capacity as creator and organiser of a new type of locomotive works, with his reputation, and that of the works, stretching round the world. All this involved pioneering the use of new technology. In view of his use of machine tools, many of them made at Crewe, to reduce production costs, the phrase "cutting edge of technology" could almost have been made for him, even though it is completely anachronistic.

In order to minimise the cost of building and maintaining the locomotive stock the use of batch production methods applied to a very limited range of designs was continued and extended. Before his arrival at Crewe an average of 30 new locomotives was constructed every year, but by 1866 the number was 74 per year. In 1870, his last full year in charge, 69 locomotives were constructed and 1770 heavy and intermediate repairs were carried out.

With the ending of locomotive construction and repairs at the old Southern Division works in Wolverton some enlargement at Crewe was inevitable, but the enlargement went much further than new repair shops and involved the installation of the new technology of steel making.

Before persuading the Board to invest in a new steel works, Ramsbottom had purchased 500 tons of rail bloom (to be rolled at Crewe) from Bessemer's own works in Sheffield. An extract from an article in the *English Mechanic* shows clearly why steel rails were such an improvement, even though they were more expensive.

". . . when rolled into rails, one of them was taken at random to put down at a part of the line where the traffic was particularly heavy. The wear of this, and the ordinary contiguous rails was carefully noted and the following are the results:-

Rail laid down May 9 1862 - in Sept. 1864 there were few signs of wear. 8,000 trucks passed over this rail in twenty-four hours; and seven million trucks in the $2^1/_3$ years covered by the report. The neighbouring iron rail put down new on the same date was turned in July; replaced in September, turned in November; a new rail Jan. 6 1863, turned March 1; new rail April 29, turned July 3; new rail Sept. 29, turned Dec. 29; new rail Feb. 16th 1864, turned April 12; new rail Aug. 6. Thus the Bessemer rail had nearly worn out both sides of seven rails! The steel rail, be it understood, not having been turned, and still in good condition."

The Bessemer steel plant installed in 1863-64 by Ramsbottom not only had a capacity of 1,000 tons of ingots per month, but was one of the first outside Bessemer's own works in Sheffield. This would, undoubtedly, have been a very expensive undertaking and, in addition, the Railway would have had to pay royalties on each ton of steel produced. How far Ramsbottom's patent on an improvement to the Bessemer converter was just that, and how far it was an attempt to minimise royalty payments is an open question.

Not content with installing one steel making process, the Siemens-Martin open hearth process, which had only been invented in 1864, was also installed. This happened in 1868, though a Siemens furnace is mentioned in the *Illustrated London News* as being in operation at the time of the royal visit in 1866.

The scale of the new developments, along with

Born 7/4/62

London and North Western Railway.

ENGINE-WORKS,

Crewe, *April 12th 1862.*

Sir,

I beg to acknowledge the receipt of minute of your Board under date 22nd March by which I learn that you have done me the honour to appoint me Supt of the whole of the Locomotive Dept of this Company.

For this substantial mark of your confidence I beg to tender my warmest thanks and to assure you that it shall be my constant study to shew that it has not been misplaced,

I remain, Sir

Your most obt Servt

J. Ramsbottom.

To the Chairman
of the Board of Directors,

Above: **Ramsbottom's letter to Richard Moon following his appointment as Locomotive Superintendent of the whole line in April 1862.** *National Archives.*

the introduction of steel making, meant that the Old Works established by Joseph Locke in 1841 on a green field site was now too small. Large extensions to the west of Crewe were built, and the Crewe to Chester main line was diverted, leaving the old main line for works use only.

In order to speed up the handling of parts and materials an 18 inch gauge railway was installed in 1862, after being authorised by the Board in October 1861. This involved the use of steam engines from the start, and was the first time steam locomotives had been used on a track gauge of less than two feet. Initially the system was small but was extended as the works grew in size. At a Board meeting in January 1863 the new narrow gauge railway was reported to be much more economical than the previous hand cart system and was to be extended to reach every shop. The importance of this 18 inch gauge railway for the development of steam powered narrow gauge railways in this country, and around the world, is enormous.

The use of high speed rope drive in the workshops for overhead traversers, and for traversing jib cranes, was another step in the constant effort to reduce labour costs and speed up production. As Ramsbottom said to the Institution of Mechanical Engineers in 1864, "The driving cords employed are soft white cotton cords $^5/_8$ inch in diameter when new, and weighing about $1^1/_2$ ounce per foot: they soon become reduced to $^9/_{16}$ inch by stretching and are found to last about eight months in constant work." "The velocity of the cord is in all cases 5000 feet per minute; and in the overhead traversers the heavy loads are lifted at the rate of 1 foot $7^1/_2$ inches per minute, the total leverage being slightly over 3000 to 1; so that in this case the driving power required to lift the maximum load of 25 tons is only 18 lbs. irrespective of friction."

This system of rope drive was still being referred to in D.K. Clark's *Manual of Rules, Tables and Data for Mechanical Engineers*, 6th edition 1891. Ramsbottom is sometimes criticised for leaving Crewe with a legacy of slow cranes, but this is to look through the wrong end of the telescope.

What matters is how much he speeded up the handling of materials while he was in charge, not his successors' failure to install faster cranes.

THE ROYAL VISIT

Crewe works received its ultimate accolade during Ramsbottom's tenure of office in 1866 when Edward, Prince of Wales, came with a large party to visit the new steel works. The occasion was described in some detail, and depicted in the *Illustrated London News*. The Prince spent about an hour and a half viewing various processes, including the Bessemer converter in action, and the operation of the 10 ton horizontal duplex steam hammer. At the end of the visit the party travelled by train to the house in Chester Place, a temporary platform having been installed to the rear of the house. There they "partook of luncheon" before travelling to the Duke of Sutherland's estate at Trentham.

Unfortunately no further details of the Royal visit to Chester Place have survived. The Court Circular for the day states that, at Trentham, a "grand dinner party took place in the splendid dining-room, in honour of the royal visit." Among the guests invited was "Mr. Ramsbottom", but not apparently Mrs. Ramsbottom. "The Duke and Duchess of Sutherland gave a grand ball in the drawing-room in the evening . . ." "Dancing commenced about ten o'clock, to the music of Messrs. Coote and Tinney's band." "Supper was served at twelve o'clock, after which dancing was resumed, and continued till half-past-two." One person notable by his absence throughout the day was the Chairman of the London and North Western Railway, Richard Moon.

INNOVATION AND STANDARDISATION

The patents taken out by Ramsbottom between 1862 and 1871 reflect the change in the nature of the job. In addition to his patent for improving the Bessemer steel making process, there are seven patents relating

VISIT OF THE PRINCE OF WALES TO THE CREWE STEELWORKS.

Above: Ramsbottom explains the use of the steel cutting saw and associated movement of materials to the Prince of Wales during his visit to Crewe in 1866. *Below:* Whilst at Crewe the Prince also saw the tyre expanding machine. *(Both) Illustrated London News.*

to the handling, hammering, and rolling, of metals, including two for his horizontal duplex steam hammer.

Another important development pioneered by Ramsbottom was the use of a direct drive reversing rolling mill. This was the subject of a paper to the Institution of Mechanical Engineers in 1866, with a site visit the following day. The cylinders were 28" in diameter by 4 feet stroke, and it was fitted with Allan straight link motion, the only instance that I have come across where Ramsbottom used this motion.

The idea of such a rolling mill was not entirely new and had been put forward by James Nasmyth some years earlier. On 4 December 1866 Nasmyth received the following letter from Ramsbottom:-

> "*Dear Sir - I must crave your forgiveness for my great delay in acknowledging the receipt of your kind letter of the 29th August, in which you refer to the successful carrying out at these works of your idea of a 'Reversing Rolling Mill without a Fly-wheel.' It has long been to me a matter of astonishment that your idea has not been reduced to practice years ago, particularly when it is considered how well the arrangement is adapted to the rolling of Armour Plates, or other work requiring a sustained effort, whilst it is at the same time more effective than the ordinary mill arrangement for very light work. So much is this latter true, that the men who are left to their own choice in the matter, will reverse the mill rather than pass a light sheet of 8 or 10 lbs. weight over the upper mill.*"

(Ramsbottom concluded by offering to show Nasmyth round Crewe.)

In addition to the machines covered by patents, many other devices and tools were developed for use at the works which were not. Some of these were shown in a series of articles about Crewe Works in the *Engineer* in the 1860s. All, however, had only one end in view - to cut the cost of production and repairs to the minimum. Ramsbottom fully recognised the importance of the interchangeability of parts, and developed

a system of working to standard gauges to an extent that was quite new at the time. These not only applied to new construction, a series of graduated sizes being adopted for the renewal of worn parts as well.

As most of the Ramsbottom designs were produced in batches over a period of years, it is necessary to take the period from 1857 to 1871 without a break in order to see the total output. During these fourteen years Crewe built 793 DX goods locos, 76 Newton class 2-4-0s, 60 Problem (or Lady of the Lake) class 2-2-2s, 50 Samson class 2-4-0s, and 20 0-6-0 tank engines. In addition to these 999 main line locomotives there were 36 0-4-0 shunting engines, and the first four 18 inch gauge works engines, a grand total of 1,039 engines.

Ramsbottom achieved a greater degree of standardisation than any British railway company before or since, as can be seen from the fact that in 1874 the DX goods class comprised 44% of the London and North Western's locomotive stock. Due to the continued construction of some Ramsbottom designs after he left, the figure for DX goods as a percentage of locomotive stock in 1871 would, probably have been slightly lower.

Ramsbottom was not only concerned about the Company's locomotives but also the engine crews. This is clear from a letter he sent to Moon on 1 March 1869 enclosing a copy of a letter which he had received from the Locomotive Foreman at Shrewsbury. This letter indicates how miserably some locomotive crews were being treated.

> "*Central Wales Railway*
> *I beg to inform you that the Co. are building houses at every Station for Station Masters and porters, & I wish to ask if you would kindly intercede of our men at Craven Arms, as it is really shocking the way some of them are sleeping & lodging - 13 in one house, & several beds are used night & day.*"

Ramsbottom was obviously shocked himself, for he added the underlining which had a loop at the end containing his own initials. In his covering letter he added:-

PARIS EXHIBITION—TEN-TON DUPLEX HAMMER.
BY MR. RAMSBOTTOM, C.E., CREWE.

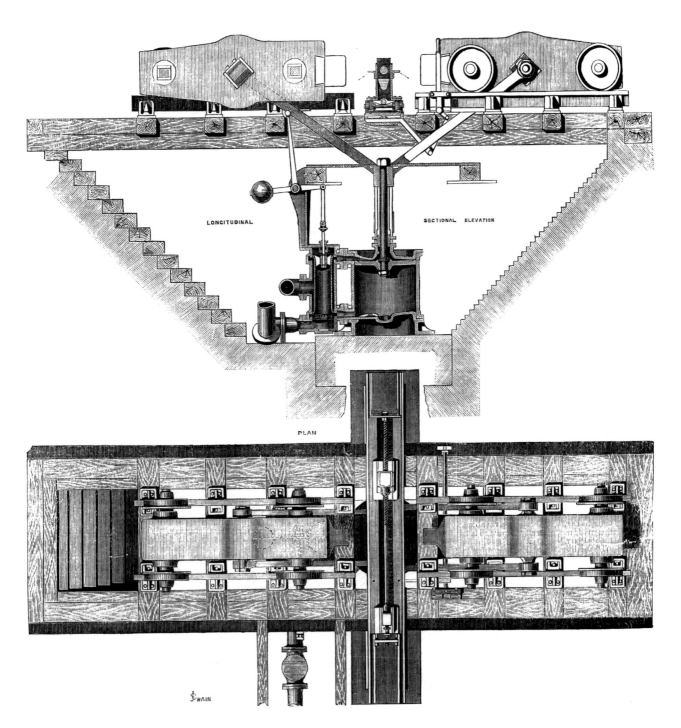

Above: An engraving from *The Engineer* of June 28th, 1867, showing Ramsbottom's 10-ton Duplex Hammer. A one-sixth scale model of the hammer was displayed at the Paris Exhibition of that year and Ramsbottom read a paper on a larger 30 ton hammer before a meeting of the Institution of Mechanical Engineers held in Paris during the exhibition. The 30-ton hammer is described in Appendix Four, Habits of Thought. *Author's Collection.*

"I may also remind you how badly we are off as regards stabling for engines at that Station."

Moon's concerns for what would now be called "shareholder value" were obviously causing problems for both engines and staff. It is interesting to note that the foreman at Shrewsbury considered Ramsbottom the person most likely to influence the Chairman.

WIDER RESPONSIBILITIES

The breadth of his responsibilities is shown by Ramsbottom's last paper to the Institution of Mechanical Engineers, and the subject of his second last patent, in 1871. This was entitled *On the Mechanical Ventilation of the Liverpool Passenger Tunnel on the London and North Western Railway.* From 1837 to 1870 the haulage of trains though the tunnel to and from Liverpool Lime Street had been by stationary engine. This system proved to be inconvenient, causing delays. "These delays, together with the increasing requirements of the

Above: **Richard Moon, Chairman of the L.N.W.R.** *L.N.W.R. Society*

ordinary traffic, at length induced the directors to remove the rope and winding engines, and to work the tunnel by locomotives in the ordinary manner; but the employment of coal-burning locomotives in a close tunnel nearly 1¼ mile long intimately connected at each end with passenger stations of great importance, was of course impracticable without a thorough and constant artificial ventilation."

The solution was to install a large air extraction system approximately half way along the tunnel, using a fan 29ft. 4ins. in diameter and 7ft. 6ins. wide., which could clear the tunnel in eight minutes. "The fan and engine are enclosed within a chimney 54 feet in diameter at the base and 23 feet at the top, rising to a height of 198 feet above the levels of the rails."

In addition to his responsibilities at the Works, Ramsbottom was also the President of the Crewe Mechanics Institute for the whole period from 1857 to 1871. With his vigorous support the Institute grew substantially. In 1861 there were 1,014 members rising to 1,933 in 1871. During this period there was great pressure for new premises with better facilities and more classrooms. After a fire in 1869 the Directors could avoid the construction of a new one no longer, costing £3,500 in total. In July 1872, shortly after his retirement, Ramsbottom was given an address in the Town Hall, paying tribute to his invaluable services, especially the way he had acted as a channel between the Institute and the Railway Company, securing much sympathy and support for the Institute. Reference is also made to Ramsbottom's contribution to the enlargement of the building, and the general quality of his leadership. He was considered to have sound judgement, to have made strenuous exertions on the Institute's behalf, and to have been extremely generous.

To give some idea of the cumulative impact of these changes on the town during Ramsbottom's years at Crewe, the workforce, which had only been 1,150 in 1851 (a mere six years before he arrived) had grown to 4,000 by 1870. The period between the 1861 and 1871 Censuses saw the population of the town of Crewe grew from

LIVERPOOL LIME STREET TUNNEL VENTILATING FAN AND CHIMNEY

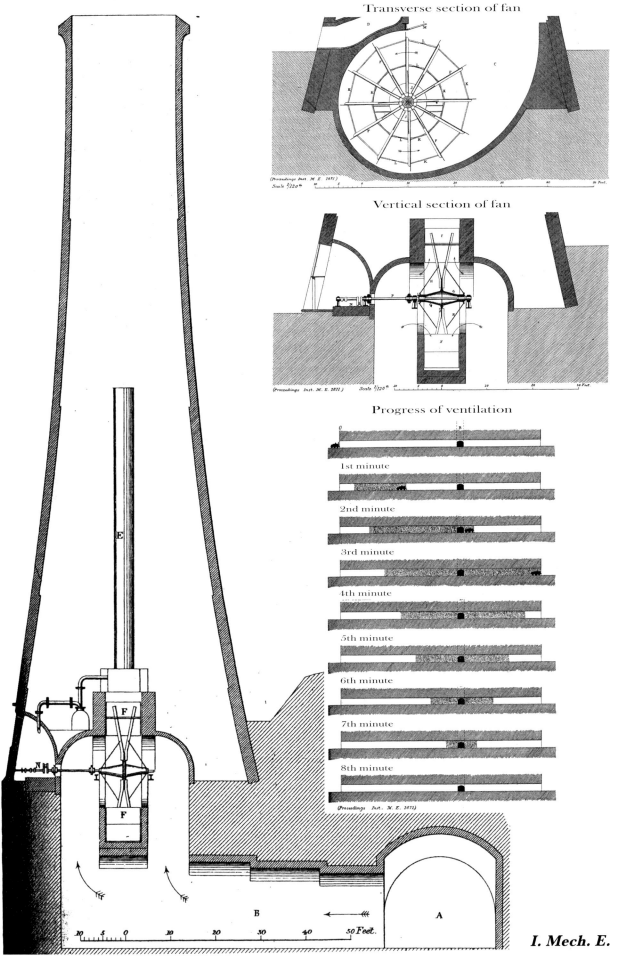

Transverse section of fan

Vertical section of fan

Progress of ventilation

0

1st minute

2nd minute

3rd minute

4th minute

5th minute

6th minute

7th minute

8th minute

I. Mech. E.

8,801 to 19,904 - an increase of 126%.

A flavour of the town can be gained from *The Encyclopaedia Britannica* (11th edition, 1910) which, in its article on Crewe, says:- "It is inhabited principally by persons in the employment of the London & North-Western railway company, and was practically created by that corporation, at a point where in 1841 only a farmhouse stood in open country. Crewe is not only one of the busiest railway stations in the world, but it is the locomotive metropolis of the London & North-Western company, which has centred here enormous workshops for the manufacture of the material and plant used in railways."

UNEXPLAINED DEPARTURE FROM CREWE

We now come to Ramsbottom's departure from Crewe. All the published material, with one exception, says that he retired on the grounds of "failing health". There is an element of truth to this, because he sent his apologies that he could not attend the 1871 summer meeting of the Institution

Above: **Ramsbottom in the ca.1870. Science Museum.**

of Mechanical Engineers. As the Institution's President he would have been expected to play a prominent part at its discussions, and meet the dignitaries of the city where the meeting was held.

The one exception to the story of "failing health" is O.S. Nock's book *The Railway Engineers.* In the last paragraph of his chapter on John Ramsbottom he explicitly states that "Ramsbottom retired a fit man." Unfortunately, it has not been possible to trace the source of this information, but it puts his departure from Crewe in a very different light.

Some of the inside story appeared in a newspaper article shortly after his death in 1897. The best thing to do is to quote from the article extensively. Unfortunately the author is anonymous, but, in view of the extensive direct quotations, the information seems to have come from the proverbial horse's mouth.

TODMORDEN TOPICS
Local Letters From An Old Contributor

Stories of the late John Ramsbottom - and they are many - spring to recollection upon reading the condensed sketches of this remarkable man's career which appeared in your last issue. To "failing health", I note, Mr.Ramsbottom's departure from Crewe is attributed; and thereby hangs a tale which, to the best of my knowledge, has never appeared in print. There was very little amiss with the great engineer's health when he left the service of the London and North Western Railway Co., although, to be sure, he was getting advanced life for an arduous position like that of chief mechanical engineer to the largest railway system of Great Britain.

Originally entering upon this work at a salary of £2,000 per year, Mr.Ramsbottom had this gradually increased, without any demur on the part of the directors, to £5,000. But, as time progressed, and the demands of the appointment grew greater, the engineer decided to insist upon a further increase of remuneration. Accordingly, at an annual meeting of the directors, he asked that his salary might be augmented, and, as this was not acceded to, he intimated that unless the directors were prepared to give an advance by the time of their next annual meeting, the year's term of notice required on either side to terminate his engagement with the Co. must be taken as coming to an end. Twelve months passed away, and when the ordinary business of the directors' meeting had reached its conclusion, Mr.Ramsbottom rose and asked the chairman what decision had been arrived at in reference to the statement he had made a year before.

Now the directors thought most highly of their chief engineer: he was the country's foremost expert in railway mechanism; and more than that, his character for loyalty and clean-handedness was beyond reproach. But, no doubt with the fear of the shareholders' criticism before their eyes, they resolutely declined to make the desired increase, and told Mr.Ramsbottom that £5,000 was as much as they were prepared to pay for his services. "Then, gentlemen," said he, "we must part: my notice, given a year ago, has now expired, and I am no longer in your employment. An older man than when I came to you, I am not unwilling to be relieved from the responsibilities of the increasing duties of this appointment. Nor is it a question of merely making more money; my affairs and those of my family are provided for. All that I have insisted upon is that the work of the position which I have held so agreeably, and, I am pleased to know, so satisfactorily to my directors, is worth an increased salary, as I pointed out to you a year ago. You think otherwise, gentlemen; well, now that I have relinquished the situation, allow me to show you something which may influence, if it does not alter, your way of looking at this question. Every gentleman in this room, and every railway man outside it, knows that I have never accepted a present nor taken a tip throughout the whole of my railway experience. That was true up to a year ago

to-night. This year it has been different. I have taken and I have kept the commissions which have been sent me. And, gentlemen," he continued, producing out of his breast pocket a bulky roll of cheques, "here they are. I must ask you to leave the secret of the signatures these cheques bear with me. Honour prevents me disclosing so much. The amounts these documents represent I wish you to understand."

Holding the bills tightly in his right hand, Mr. Ramsbottom suffered the sums enumerated in the figures at their left corners to be seen and noted, when it was found that the total reached the enormous amount of £23,000. "You see there," he concluded, "what has been sent in a single year to a man who has never been known to take a penny from anybody in this way. The contractors' commissions come to between £20,000 and £25,000. You say that the office is not worth more than £5,000! Is that your opinion now?" As he rolled the cheques together, an excited director almost screamed out that they were the property of the Company. Mr.Ramsbottom smiled, and bending down from the mantel-piece against which he had been leaning, put the bundle of bills into the heart of the red-hot coals in the grate, and held it there with the heel of his boot until the whole of the £23,000 had burned to ashes and mingled with the smoke of the chimney.

What this article shows is a man who felt very strongly that he had been wronged, and was definitely not going to retire quietly. Why he felt such a display of righteous indignation was called for can only be a matter of conjecture, but the situation that annoyed him must have been going on for some time or else he would not have collected the cheques he had been sent for a whole year. As he obviously did not cash them, he did not take the money offered, and so did not break his principles by holding on to the cheques.

It is also valuable because, for once, we seem to have the actual words of John Ramsbottom, not just statements about him, nor does it convey the impression of a sick man. There are many details including him holding the notes in his right hand while leaning against a mantle-piece, and the screaming director, which can only have come from someone who was there. The most likely person is a close friend of Ramsbottom himself. Presumably that person wrote at a later date to a friend or relative in Todmorden who eventually gave the information to the press.

Unravelling the situation is made more complicated by the fact that Richard Moon had been working behind the scenes to bring back Francis Webb, his former second in command, from the Bolton Iron and Steel Co. where he had gone in 1866 ending up as a managing partner. Not only that, but Thomas Stubbs, whom Ramsbottom had appointed Chief Draughtsman at 25 and Indoor Assistant (Works Manager) at 30, died after a three week illness on 16 September.

Moon seems to have contacted Webb immediately. On 8 October 1870 he sent Webb the following letter:-

"I took the opportunity as agreed of naming to our Special Commte what had passed with reference to your rejoining our Comp. as Locomotive Superintendent.

1st that the salary should be £2,000 for the 1st year and £3,000 afterwards. We thought that the notice had best be as in the case of Mr. Ramsbottom, twelve months, and that the number of pupils if you take any, for your own comfort as well as ours, should be limited to four.

You know the regulations of the Co. as to patents and other matters, so that I need not trouble you with them here.

I do not know what rent Mr. Ramsbottom pays for his house, but you can have it on the same terms as he has had it.

I mentioned to the Commte that you could not leave your friends with whom you are at present for about 6 months, but that you may possibly arrange to leave them at an earlier period. We shall be ready for you whenever you can make arrangements to join us, and perhaps you will let me know after seeing your friends.

The Special Commte unanimously agreed to my proposal, and Mr. Chance, the Chairman of the Locomotive Commte desired me to say that it has his special concurrence.

Hoping that you may have a long and promising career."

As this letter was written months before Ramsbottom's illness in the summer of 1871, it takes on a distinctly darker tone if one accepts that he was a fit man in 1870 rather than a semi-invalid. It also shows no sign of regret whatever that Ramsbottom was having to leave Crewe, in fact the reverse.

Ramsbottom's last public appearance as Locomotive Superintendent of the London and North Western Railway was at his farewell dinner at the Euston hotel in late September 1871. This is mentioned in the *Railway Reminiscences* of G.P. Neele, for many years Superintendent of the Line, and was also the subject of a short article in *The Engineer.* Richard Moon, the company Chairman presided, and among the guests were the Duke of Buckingham, Sir Joseph Whitworth, the Lord Mayor of London, Charles Beyer, and others. "About forty gentlemen sat down" as the article puts it.

In replying to the toast "The health of Mr. Ramsbottom" proposed by Richard Moon, Ramsbottom said he regretted that the present state of his health had compelled him to retire from a position that he had the honour to hold for many years. It would be interesting to know how many people believed him. The report in *The Engineer* of Ramsbottom's speech, and any stories put about by Moon and his allies, appear to be the origin of the belief that his health was in permanent decline after his illness in the summer. The contrary is in fact the case; if Ramsbottom had been seriously unwell, whether physically or mentally, the L.N.W.R. would have been apologising for not having an official dinner at the Euston hotel rather than having one.

It is now difficult to find evidence in Crewe of the man whose fourteen years in charge stimulated the greatest change and growth within the town. There is, however, a memorial in the company church, Christ Church. This is a stained-glass window installed by the Ramsbottom family in 1902 (see photograph inside rear cover).

Ramsbottom received three testimonials on leaving Crewe - two from the railway staff, and one from the Board. Of the two from the staff one was an illuminated address on vellum, in a carved oak casket, from the Mechanics Institute, and the other was a book of signatures which had been sent round all the sheds. The testimonial from the Board was an elaborate confection of silver and silver gilt (see picture), and was sent as an example of British workmanship to the Vienna Exhibition of 1873.

Above: **The shareholders of the L.N.W.R. voted £500 for a testimonial to Ramsbottom on his retirement. It took the form of a pedestal on a plinth supported by four columns on which Science is holding Hercules in chains while pointing to a plan of Crewe. The pedestal has four medallion portraits, one of which is Ramsbottom under whose portrait is the inscription "To J. Ramsbottom, in acknowledgement of great talents, rare qualities, and eminent services. The London and North Western Railway Company. R. Moon, Chairman." It was made by Messrs. Elkington but its size and present whereabouts are unknown.**

Above: This large grindstone in the Old Works had a saddle seat for the operator. The Health and Safety Executive might take a dim view of it! *L.N.W.R. Society.* *Above right:* A bolt making machine in the Old Works dating from Ramsbottom's time. *National Railway Museum. Opposite page top:* A mid-1870s view along the centre bay of Ramsbottom's new boiler shop opened in 1870. *L.N.W.R. Society.*

Below: **The Old Works, stores and office block around 1880. The erecting shops were originally built as steam sheds, hence the roof ventilation. The footbridge on the right leads to the Grease Works.** *L.N.W.R. Society.*

Above: Ramsbottom's rope driven hornblock grinding machine of the 1860s could dress all twelve faces of this DX goods chassis simultaneously. *L.N.W.R. Society.*
Below left: The Old Works forge contained a number of steam hammers dating from the Ramsbottom period. The 10 ton duplex was in service until November 1896 and the 30 ton duplex lasted until September 1898. *L.N.W.R. Society.*

Opposite page top: Drawings of Crewe Works narrow gauge engine, *Tiny*, were published in *Engineering*, 19th January, 1866. *L.N.W.R. Society.*

Opposite page bottom: A view of *Tiny* at work outside the Old Works around 1880. The engine survived until May 1928. A total of seven steam locos (*Tiny, Pet, Nipper, Topsy, Midge, Billy* and *Dickie*) were built between 1862 and 1876, five to Ramsbottom's design, and two to a Webb design. All were withdrawn by 1931 and replaced by one new diesel loco, named *Crewe*, which lasted to the mid-1950s. *L.N.W.R. Society.*

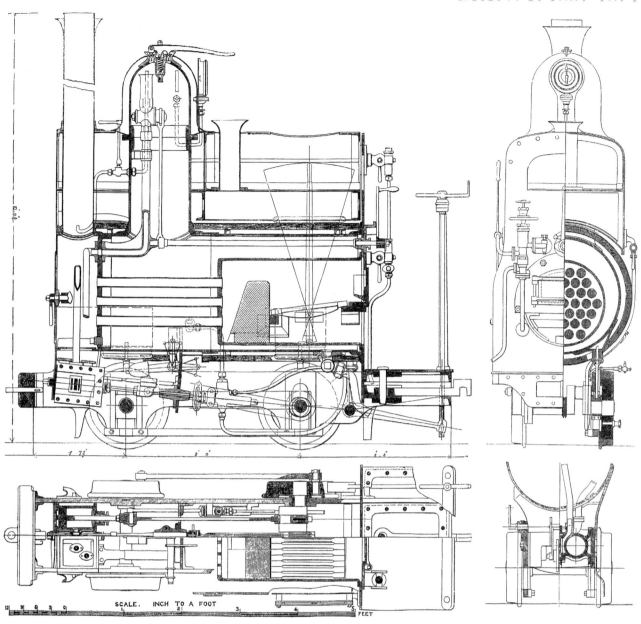

SCALE. INCH TO A FOOT

FEET

Above: Inside No. 2 erecting shop with locomotive repair work going: note Ramsbottom's rope driven overhead cranes. *L.N.W.R. Society.*

Below: The chimneys of the 1864 steel melting plant can be seen behind the partially complete steel rail mill. This view dates from 1874. *L.N.W.R. Society.*

Above: From 1869 to 1875 there was extensive new building work going on and Ramsbottom set up several brick making plants using clay sub-soil adjacent to the Works. The new buildings in the background are the boiler shop on the left and boiler yard smithy on the right. *L.N.W.R. Society.*

Below and overleaf: Ramsbottom designed the Problem class 2-2-2 in 1859 for express passenger use and No. 565 is seen here when new in works grey livery, outside No. 2 erecting shop. Overleaf is a sectioned drawing of the class taken from *Locomotive Engineering and the Mechanism of Railways* by Zerah Colburn, published in 1871 (see also Appendix One). *L.N.W.R. Society and I. Mech. E.*

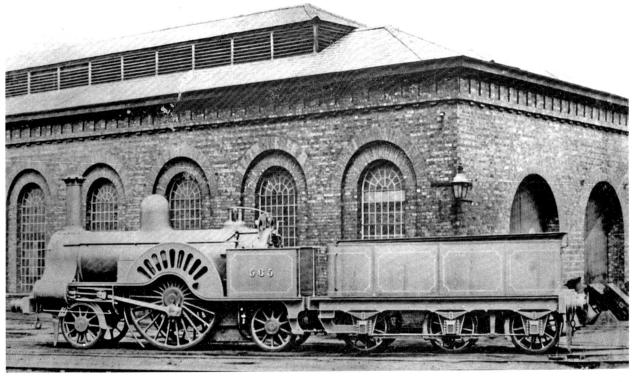

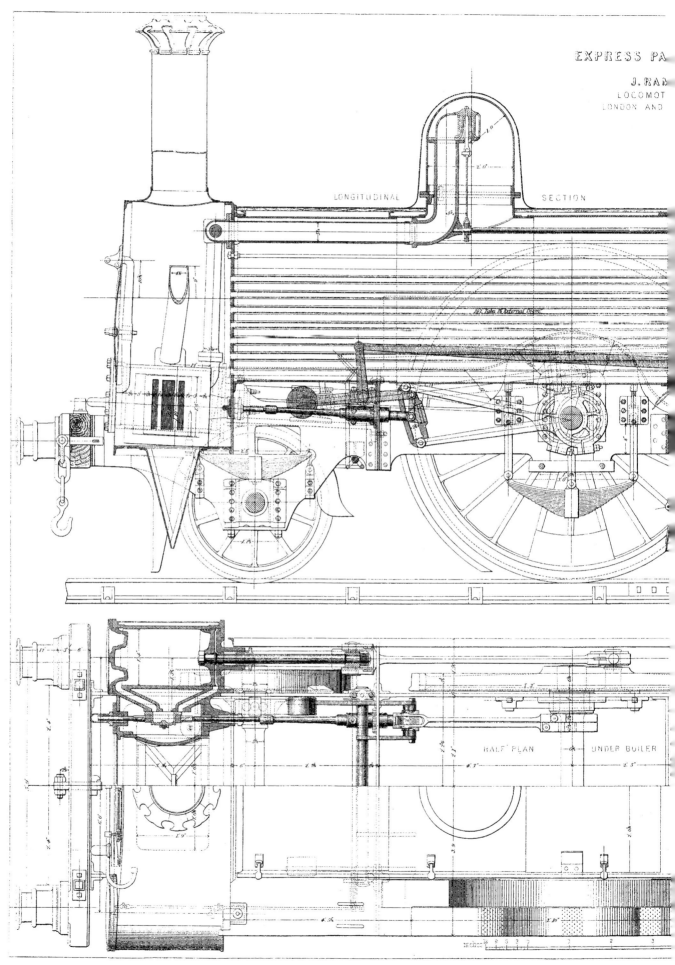

EXPRESS PA

J. RA

LOCOMOT

LONDON AND

LONGITUDINAL   SECTION

Nº Tube M Internal Diam

HALF PLAN   UNDER BOILER

inches

WILLIAM COLLINS, SONS &

42

Plate II

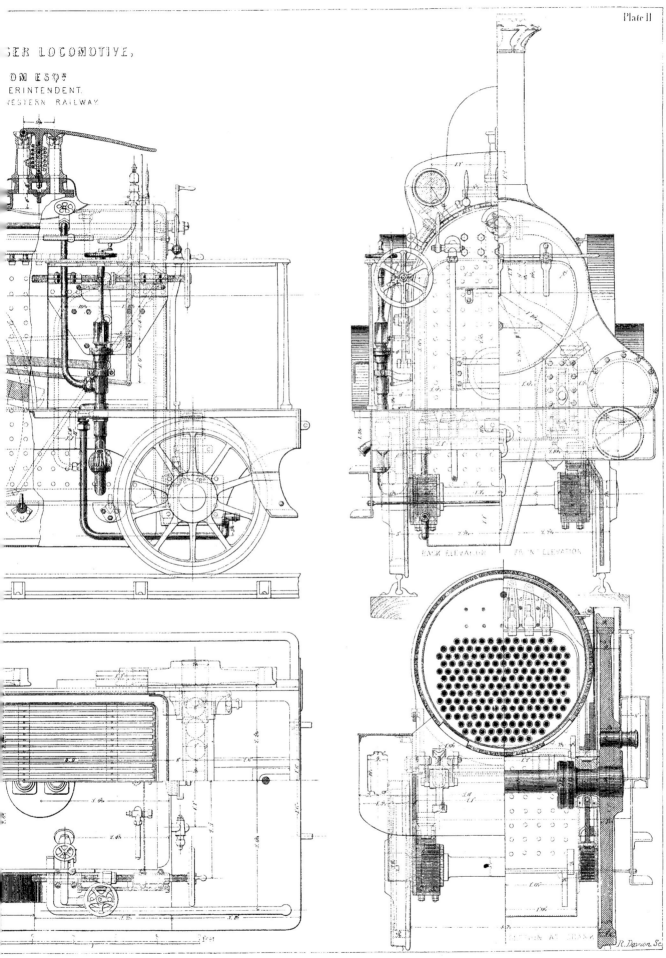

GER LOCOMOTIVE,

OM ESQ.
ERINTENDENT.
WESTERN RAILWAY

N. GLASGOW. & EDINBURGH.

Above: DX goods engine No. 578 was photographed in 1862 with its crew in formal pose. The engine is painted in Ramsbottom's lined green livery. Some early members of the class were named whilst others, including this one, had a splasher mounted brass plate bearing the engine number. *L.N.W.R. Society.*

Below: One of ten Ramsbottom "Newton" class 2-4-0 passenger engines built by the L.N.W.R for the Lancashire & Yorkshire Railway in 1873. By that date Webb had made some minor changes, most notably the protective cab. Seven of them were numbered 456 - 463 and allocated to the L. & Y. section, three were sent to the East Lancashire section and numbered 731 - 733. No. 731 had an illustrious career becoming the motive power for the L. & Y.'s Chief Mechanical Engineer's saloon. It was not withdrawn until 1926. *Noel Coates Collection.*

Above: Chester Place was the official residence of successive Locomotive Engineers from Ramsbottom to Beames. The pleasant surroundings are illusory as it was but a stone's throw from the works (see plan below and map overleaf).

Below left: Ramsbottom in the centre of this group on a visit to Chester Place in 1885. His successor, F.W. Webb, is on the right. *Both L.N.W.R. Society.*

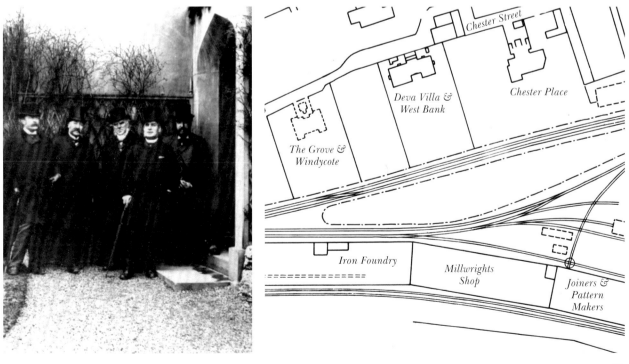

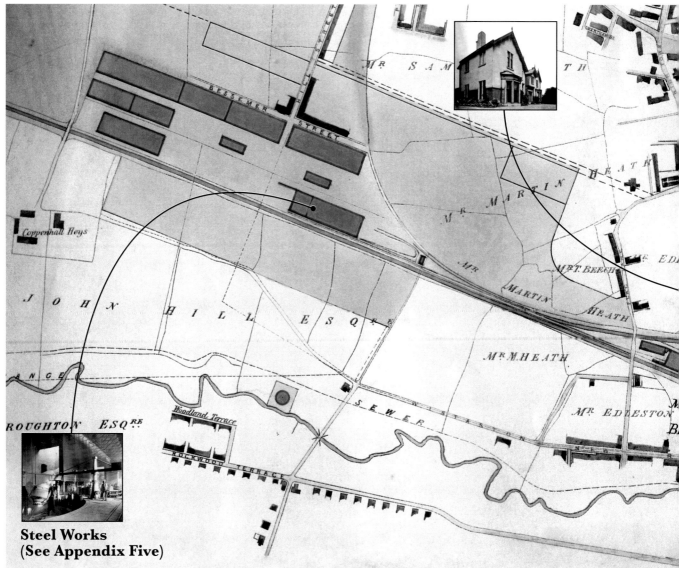

Steel Works
(See Appendix Five)

PLAN OF CREWE.

Scale 1 Foot =1 Mile.

CREWE WORKS, APRIL, 7TH 1868.

Correct as regards the Co.s property only up to the above date May 1st 1873.

L.& N.W.R. Co.s Land coloured thus
Loco & Steel Works.
Other Buildings.

When Ramsbottom arrived at Crewe in 1857 the Works comprised the area marked as "Old Works" and the three buildings in red directly below it, situated between the two lines to the west of Crewe station. The buildings in the angle between the main line to the north and the Manchester line were brought into the Locomotive Department in 1860 from the Carriage and Wagon Departments. Other buildings in red to the north and west of the Chester line, including the "Steel Works", were built or authorised during Ramsbottom's period in charge. This plan clearly indicates the scale of the expansion achieved between 1857 and 1871. The southerly line from Crewe Station towards Chester (opened in 1868), was put in to facilitate this expansion, and to separate internal Works movements from trains on the Chester main line. In view of the areas of the plan with landowners' names but shaded in pink, it is clear that the L.N.W.R. was buying large areas of land after the plan was originally drawn in 1868 with a view to the future expansion of the Works.

Courtesy of David Patrick.

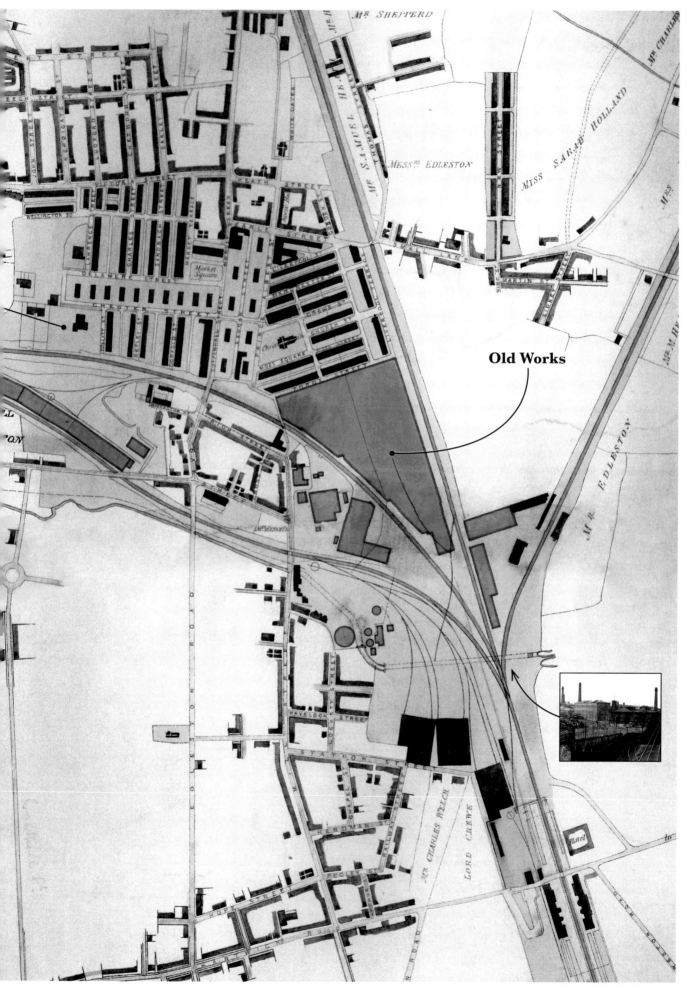

Old Works

INDIAN SUMMER

After leaving Crewe John Ramsbottom was put on a retainer of £1,000 per annum by the L.N.W.R. for several years, ostensibly because of his "great ability and mechanical genius". This was an astute move by Richard Moon and the Board because it achieved two different ends. Firstly, it would have avoided the Directors being criticised at shareholders' meetings for losing one of their greatest assets and, secondly, it would have prevented Ramsbottom from saying anything in public about the reasons for his departure from the L.N.W.R.

In 1873 he established the Ramsbottom Scholarship, worth £40 per annum, at the Owens College in Manchester. This was tenable for two years, and was to be competed for by young men employed in the locomotive department of the London and North Western Railway. The scholarship survived for over a hundred years, keeping the name of Ramsbottom alive at Crewe, even though he was persona non grata with Richard Moon.

Little information has come to light about the consultancy work he was doing in the period from 1871 onwards, but records show that he was used to arbitrate on at least three occasions by railway companies in dispute. The first involved the Great Northern Railway, the second the Cheshire Lines Committee and the third involved a dispute between the Manchester Sheffield and Lincolnshire Railway and the South Yorkshire Railway. As several of his patents had not expired at the time he retired, these may have been a useful source of income.

By the 1870s Edward Watkin, formerly an assistant to Mark Huish, had acquired a knighthood and become the Chairman of three separate railway companies. These were the Manchester, Sheffield and Lincolnshire; the South Eastern; and the Metropolitan Railways. In 1873 Watkin asked Ramsbottom, in the light of his experience at the Lime Street tunnel in Liverpool, to find out if some method of artificial ventilation could be applied on the Metropolitan Railway, allowing trains to be hauled by different

Opposite page: **Owens College in Manchester was founded in 1851 with the bequest of local industrialist, John Owens. It was non-religious and Owens' instructions were that "The institution shall be open to all applicants for admission without respect to place of birth, and without distinction of rank or condition in society."** *University of Manchester.*

types of locomotive. Ramsbottom's response was that the coal they were using was nearly as smokeless as coke, and that, as far as ventilation was concerned, he could not find grounds to recommend a change unless there were an increase in traffic requiring [unspecified] mechanisms to overcome the difficulty.

In his capacity as Chairman of the South Eastern Railway, Watkin called upon Ramsbottom on two occasions for advice. The first was in 1875 and concerned the question of new locomotives for the railway (see Appendix Five - The "Ramsbottom" Ironclads), and the second was in 1885 when he sought advice on enlarged water cranes which would enable engines to take water in the time that it took to set down and pick up passengers.

In 1876 Ramsbottom's friend of nearly forty years, Charles Beyer, died at his large house near Llantysilio in North Wales, leaving him as one of the three executors. Beyer left nearly £109,000 in total to Owens College (now University of Manchester). Ramsbottom, along with Henry Robertson, another of the executors and a partner in Beyer, Peacock & Co., not only carried out their obligations under the will but, in view of the clear intention in Beyer's will that the bulk of his estate should go to the College, were prepared to surrender monies to the College that they could themselves have kept. This involved Ramsbottom in foregoing the sum of £3,192/12s/9d. At a time when average industrial wages were no more than £1 per week, this £3,000 would have represented a lifetime's earnings for many. The fact that he was prepared to give it up indicates not only that he could afford to do so, but how high the regard was that he had for Charles Beyer.

In 1877 he was appointed a life governor of Owens College in Manchester, and gave considerable assistance in expanding the mechanical engineering department in line with the terms of Beyer's will. Further expansion in the 1880s included an early gas engine for demonstration purposes. The professor, Osborne Reynolds, acknowledged his considerable assistance in the design of the steam engine laboratory in around 1885. Apart from his connection with the engineering department, he was "a generous contributor to the fund for building a medical school" at the College.

The Ramsbottom Trip Gear, which he patented in 1880, was used in conjunction with the Corliss valves which were common on stationary engines at the end of the nineteenth century. It was his twenty-third and last patent. A form of this trip gear is mentioned in D.K. Clark's *The Steam Engine* of 1890 and was fitted to the two engines described in the book which were manufactured by his Goodfellow relations. Given the family connection, it may be that the Goodfellows would have been able to strike a better financial deal with Ramsbottom than with other patent

Above: **Charles Beyer.** *From a painting by the Chevalier Schmid.* **University of Manchester.**

holders, but this is merely a surmise.

In 1883 Beyer, Peacock & Co. had become a limited company, buying out the old partnership, but including Richard Peacock and Henry Robertson as Directors of the new private limited company. John Ramsbottom is listed as being a Director from the very beginning, but it is difficult to establish his level of day to day involvement because the Beyer, Peacock archive in Manchester does not contain any Board minutes or other papers from the private company. In the light of his pioneering use of a steam operated 18 inch gauge railway to service Crewe works twenty years earlier, it is not surprising that within a few years of him becoming a Director an 18 inch gauge railway had been installed to serve the works in Gorton.

Despite having left the L.N.W.R. under what seems to have been the vast cloud of official company hostility, Ramsbottom obviously continued to have the respect of his colleagues in the Institution of Mechanical Engineers. While he read no further papers, he did make contributions to debates on several occasions, and as a past President was automatically on the Council of the Institution.

The contributions he made were on a variety of topics, not all to do with railway matters - in 1872 on marine engines, in 1874 on hydraulic power, in 1878 on the cost of railway traffic, in 1879 on fireless locomotives for tramways, in 1882 on an automatic screw brake, and also a centrifugal separator, and in 1884 on the French "Decauville" narrow gauge railways, and on compounding in locomotives.

This last contribution is interesting because it contains no reference at all to the L.N.W.R. or to the Webb compounds. Ramsbottom's position was that he had no experience whatever of compound locomotives; that it was "pretty nearly a tie" "as between the best ordinary locomotive, and the compound locomotive working at the same initial pressure"; and that it would be necessary to generate steam at a substantially higher pressure "in order to show the advantages of the compound system when applied to railway working". Technically he was correct because the temperature range possible between a typical marine boiler pressure of 80 to 90 p.s.i. and the 2 or 3 p.s.i. absolute of a condenser would have been much greater than that between a typical 140 p.s.i. and atmospheric pressure possible in a railway locomotive. His comments, however, would be hardly likely to sustain a warm relationship with the increasingly autocratic Francis Webb, his successor at Crewe.

Below: **Beyer, Peacock maker's plate on the splasher of preserved Lancashire & Yorkshire Railway 0-6-0 No. 957, Beyer Works No. 2840.** *John Hesselwood.*

HORWICH,
THE LAST GREAT WORK

esides accepting a directorship at Beyer, Peacock's, Ramsbottom was also asked in 1883 by the recently appointed Chairman and Chief Executive of the Lancashire and Yorkshire Railway, John Pearson, to act as consultant for a year on the railway's works and repair facilities. A fit 69 years old, this involved him in visiting all the sheds, and the two works at Miles Platting and Bury, with W. Barton Wright, the Locomotive Superintendent. Wright had been dissatisfied with the facilities at his disposal for several years, and the Board accepted Ramsbottom's report in February 1884, creating the impetus for a new works. The salient points were these:

"That

the work of the Locomotive department divides itself into two great branches, namely the Indoor and the Outdoor, i.e. building-and-repairs, and running."

"That

the Works at Miles Platting and Bury were inadequate and incapable of expansion. They could not properly cope with repairs, let alone the building of engines which he advised. As an example of the archaic facilities, the L&Y had two overhead cranes for 925 engines, compared with Crewe's 32

cranes for 2,419 engines."

"That

all but four of the steam sheds were too small and were further hampered by devoting some of their meagre space to repair work which should be done in one central Works."

"That

he found Mr. Wright fully alive to the importance of standardisation on four or five types of heavier modern engines and he thought the types designed would successfully meet the growing needs of the service."

Other points to be taken into consideration were the price of labour, a good water supply, cheap coal, and a central location to minimise light engine running.

This is the report that led to the period that could with justification be said to be Ramsbottom's last great achievement - the planning and building of a wholly new works on a green field site. This was not only a personal achievement, but created a legacy that lasted for very nearly one hundred years.

Ramsbottom and Wright were requested to inspect suitable sites and report back to the next Board meeting. Their tour of the Lancashire and Yorkshire Railway covered sites

Previous page: **A batch of Aspinall 2-4-2 tank engines under construction in the Horwich erecting shops during the first few years of operation.** *L.Y.R.S. Collection.* **Below: A panoramic view across the west end of the works. The individual shops can be identified from the plan on page 57. The tall building on the skyline above the office block is the Mechanics Institute.** *Noel Coates Collection.*

at Broadfield, Bury, Moston, Castleton, Mirfield, Brighouse, Horbury Junction, and some on the Wakefield to Goole line. Other sites were suggested for investigation by directors and these were discussed on 21 May.

The Land Agent of the Company said at this meeting that an estate at Horwich (350 or 650 acres depending on sources) would be sold at the Mitre Hotel, Manchester, by auction on 27 May. Ramsbottom, Wright and the Agent were requested to inspect the site and report to a special meeting to be held on 26 May, unless they felt the site was unsuitable. Their report was favourable and the Land Agent was instructed to purchase the estate for the company for a sum not exceeding £65,000. At the auction it was secured for only £36,000.

After dealing daily with the difficulties caused by Crewe Works being spread out along the Chester main line, it must have come as something of a relief to be able to plan the new Works on a compact site which still left room for future expansion. Ramsbottom submitted drawings on 26 September showing the positions proposed for the various works departments. He also advised the erection of the main office first, and that the foundations should be put in as soon as possible so that building could start in the spring of 1885. Such was the speed at which the works was being planned that it had already been stated in the local Bolton press that the erecting shop would be 1,520 feet long, which it was.

The question of how the buildings were to be heated was another problem that Ramsbottom considered. His advice was to use hot water pipes, utilising heat from exhaust steam generated within the works. After an inspection by Ramsbottom and Wright it was concluded that only about half the machine tools and equipment in Miles Platting and Bury would be suitable for the new works.

It would be interesting to know whether

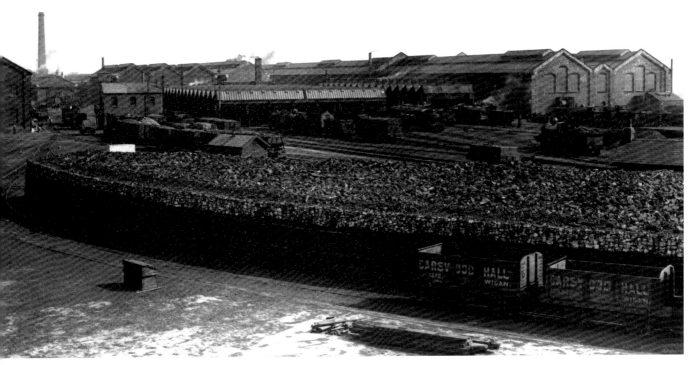

Ramsbottom managed all this planning within the confines of his study, or whether he created domestic chaos by covering the floors of his home in Alderley Edge with large scale plans and diagrams, while he worked out the proper relationship between the various parts of the works. Without being unduly fanciful one can imagine Mrs. Ramsbottom being pleased that her husband had a big project to get his teeth into, while being concerned at the level of domestic upheaval that the plans entailed.

After his consultancy had been extended for a further year in 1884, Ramsbottom was invited in September 1885 to become a member of the Lancashire & Yorkshire Railway Board, in succession to Lord Houghton. According to the anonymous *Todmorden Topics* article published after his death, he initially declined the seat on the Board because he did not possess the requisite number of shares to qualify. This objection was overcome by Samuel Fielden, of Centre Vale, Todmorden, transferring sufficient shares into his name to allow him to take up the vacant directorship. This gift is evidence of early links with Todmorden being maintained.

In his new position as a Director, and Chairman of the Locomotive Works, and Rolling Stock Committees, Ramsbottom was in a position to deal directly with contractors at the Horwich site, and to guarantee that modern machine tools were installed at the outset. In view of his comment about overhead cranes it is worth noting that in March 1885 he, with Wright, was ordering twenty 30-ton overhead cranes for Horwich from Hetherington & Co. of Manchester. Once again an 18 inch gauge railway was installed to service the works. (It is surely no coincidence that the three works which used 18 inch gauge railways are all ones with which he was associated.)

The orderly development of the plans for the works was temporarily threatened in June 1886 when Wright decided to return to India. John Aspinall, who had been one of Ramsbottom's premium apprentices at Crewe, was speedily appointed as Chief Mechanical Engineer in July 1886, taking up the position on 1 October. He had been Locomotive Superintendent of the

Great Southern and Western Railway in Ireland since 1882.

Within six weeks Aspinall was asked to report to the Board on the work which needed to be done at Horwich. One point he was very clear on was the advantages the company would gain from manufacturing its own steel, including a reduction in the capital value of stocks of raw materials. Ramsbottom, quoting from his own experience, was able to give an example where a crankshaft bought in from an outside maker cost £67, whereas one made at Crewe had cost £19/10s/4½d. He estimated that there would be saving by producing steel at Horwich of £4 to £5 per ton, and that the steel works would cost £15,000 to £20,000.

In the light of these recommendations, it is not surprising that a steel works was planned and installed at Horwich. This largely followed current practice at Crewe with a full complement of gas producers, gas fired furnaces, and a steel foundry. By using the Siemens-Martin open hearth process the Railway was able to convert the old locomotives which it scrapped into new ones in a short space of time, with only a small quantity of new pig-iron being required for each batch of steel.

The relationship between Aspinall and Ramsbottom was obviously crucial to the success of the development of Horwich Works, and it is interesting to note that Aspinall was always happy to give Ramsbottom the credit for selecting the site, and laying out the broad lines of its development.

Ramsbottom's old friend Sir Joseph Whitworth died in 1887 while staying in Monte Carlo. While Ramsbottom was not one of the executors, he was consulted by them about the best ways to ensure that Whitworth's intentions were fulfilled.

In 1888 Ramsbottom received his only academic recognition in the form of an honorary degree of Master in Engineering from the University of Dublin - effectively from Trinity College Dublin. The Library at Trinity, unfortunately, does not have a record of any citation made at the time the degree was conferred, nor have they been able to indicate who made the recommendation

Above: Before the opening of Horwich works the L. & Y. purchased engines from a number of manufacturers, including Beyer, Peacock. No. 758 was one of a batch of fifty built in 1881/82; all were later converted to saddle tanks. *Manchester Museum of Science and Industry (M.M.S.I.).*

Below and bottom: Ramsbottom was a Director of Beyer, Peacock before and during his time on the Board of the L. & Y. To alleviate a shortage of engines whilst Horwich was under construction a batch of thirty 4-4-0s, the last L. & Y. engines from an outside maker, was built by Beyer, Peacock during 1888 and 1889. The final engine, No. 1007, was built in April 1889, some two months after No. 1008, the first new engine built at Horwich. *M.M.S.I. and L.Y.R.S. Collection.*

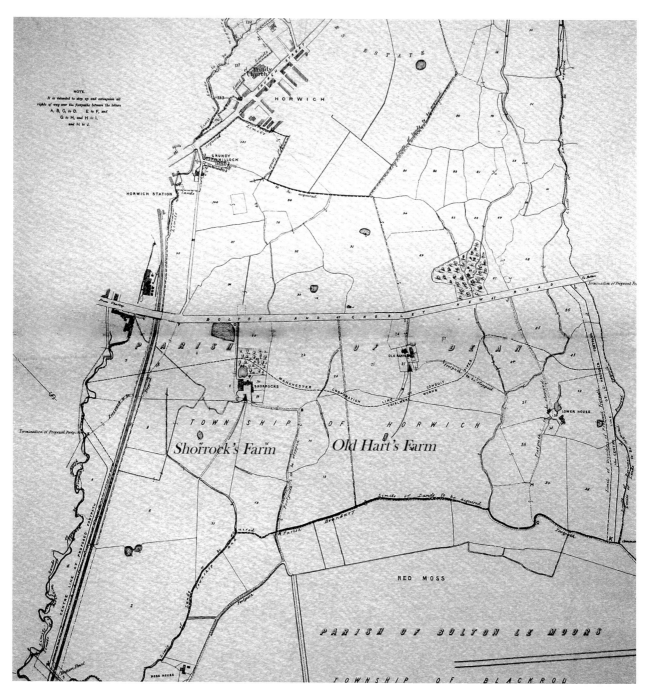

Above: This map, showing Horwich before the building of the works, was part of the Lancashire & Yorkshire Railway's deposited Parliamentary plans. The boundaries of the land to be acquired (marked on the map as "limits") are shown by dashed lines, and the footpaths to be re-routed are also shown. The estate purchased was far larger than was needed for the works, and the area to the north of Chorley New Road was sold off for housing, more than recouping the purchase price of £36,000. The Horwich branch had been opened in 1868, and the works site was bordered by the railway to the west, and Chorley New Road. The buildings at Shorrock's Farm were used as offices and stores in the early stages of site preparation. The levelling of the whole site was complete by September 1886, even though this had required the removal of some 450,000 tons of earth - the large hill around Old Hart's Farm. In 1881 the town of Horwich, which had mostly developed round the parish church, had a population of 3,761: by the time of the 1891 Census, when the works was complete and fully operational, this had risen to 12,850. *Noel Coates Collection*

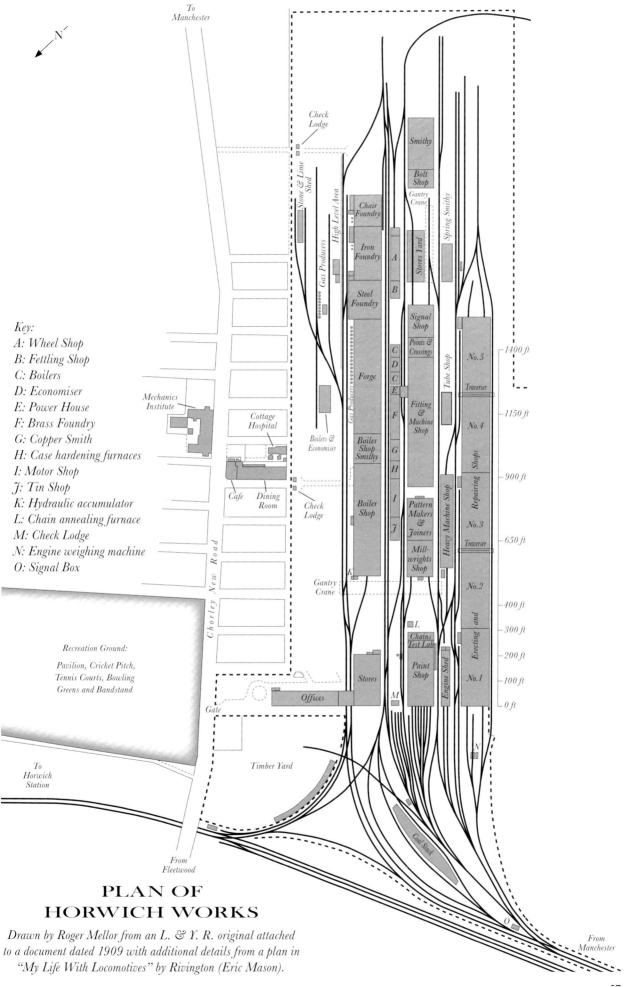

To Manchester

N

Check Lodge

Stone & Lime Shed

High Level Area

Gas Producers

Smithy

Bolt Shop

Gantry Crane

Chair Foundry

Spring Smithy

Iron Foundry

Stores Yard

A

B

Steel Foundry

Signal Shop

Points & Crossings

Tube Shop

No.5

— *1400 ft*

Traverser

Key:

A: Wheel Shop
B: Fettling Shop
C: Boilers
D: Economiser
E: Power House
F: Brass Foundry
G: Copper Smith
H: Case hardening furnaces
I: Motor Shop
J: Tin Shop
K: Hydraulic accumulator
L: Chain annealing furnace
M: Check Lodge
N: Engine weighing machine
O: Signal Box

C
D
E

Forge

F

G

H

I

J

Fitting & Machine Shop

Mechanics Institute

Cottage Hospital

Boilers & Economiser

Boiler Shop Smithy

Boiler Shop

Pattern Makers & Joiners

Heavy Machine Shop

No.4

— *1150 ft*

Repairing Shops

No.3

— *900 ft*

Traverser

— *650 ft*

Mill-wrights Shop

No.2

Cafe

Dining Room

Check Lodge

K

Gantry Crane

L

Chains Test Lab

Erecting and

— *400 ft*
— *300 ft*
— *200 ft*

Chorley New Road

Recreation Ground:

Pavilion, Cricket Pitch, Tennis Courts, Bowling Greens and Bandstand

Paint Shop

Engine Shed

No.1

— *100 ft*

— *0 ft*

Stores

M

Offices

Gate

N

To Horwich Station

Timber Yard

Coal Stack

From Fleetwood

O

From Manchester

PLAN OF HORWICH WORKS

Drawn by Roger Mellor from an L. & Y. R. original attached to a document dated 1909 with additional details from a plan in "My Life With Locomotives" by Rivington (Eric Mason).

that he should be awarded the degree. The most obvious possibility is that the recommendation was made by H.A. Ivatt, his former pupil at Crewe, who was in 1888 the Locomotive Superintendent of the Great Southern and Western Railway in Ireland, in succession to John Aspinall.

The award of the degree coincided with the Institution of Mechanical Engineers summer meeting being held in Dublin. The President of the Institution that year was Mr. Edward Hamer Carbutt. Carbutt seems to have been something of a supporter of Ramsbottom's. Not only had he persuaded Ramsbottom to speak in 1884 about the Crewe narrow gauge railway system during the discussion on the "Decauville" tramway, but on this occasion, after a paper on brewery tramways and rolling stock, he opened the discussion by referring to the 18 inch gauge railways at Crewe and said that "he thought the distinction which had been conferred upon Mr. Ramsbottom by the University of Dublin . . . was a well-deserved honour, if for no other reason than those small locomotives".

It is sadly not possible to draw a full picture of Ramsbottom's private life and family relationships because family papers do not appear to have survived. However, according to O.S. Nock, Ramsbottom was "a charming personality, and a generous contributor to the proceedings of engineering societies". This is confirmed by reports that in the heyday of cycling in the early 1890s, Professor Osborne Reynolds, and some of his students from Owens College, occasionally used to cycle out to Ramsbottom's home at Alderley Edge (see photo p.94) for a Sunday afternoon outing.

Below: **John Ramsbottom in the early 1890s.** *Courtesy of Roger Birch.*

THE FINAL YEARS

Ramsbottom's last appearance at a meeting of the Institution of Mechanical Engineers was in 1894 when he was nearly 80. The annual summer meeting was held in Manchester, and at a dinner of the Institution on 1 August he proposed a toast to "The Owens College". His son John Goodfellow Ramsbottom became an Associate Member of the Institution in the same year.

After he caught a chill whilst visiting Blackpool in the autumn of 1896, at the age of 82, he wrote to the Board of the Lancashire and Yorkshire Railway to say that he wished to resign, but they persuaded him to stay on. As he did not recover he eventually tendered his resignation in the spring of 1897 only a few weeks before he died. His death certificate gives the cause as "senility" (in this context meaning old age) and states that he had had a weak heart for the previous two years.

Fortunately, details of the funeral arrangements were given in the obituary published in the *Todmorden Advertiser,* of which his cousin Richard Chambers was still the proprietor. The funeral took place at Macclesfield Cemetery, and there was a large number of mourners - family, friends, and professional colleagues, and all men. The Lancashire and Yorkshire Railway was well represented, sending three people, including "Mr. H.A. Hoy, representing Mr. J.A.F. Aspinall, mechanical engineering department". The London and North Western Railway, by contrast, sent precisely no-one, showing that the hostility of the L.N.W.R. establishment had not decreased after twenty-six years, not even after Sir Richard Moon (as he had become) ceased being Chairman in 1891.

In August, the Lancashire and Yorkshire Railway's half yearly report contained the following: "It is with deep regret that the directors have to record the loss, during the last half year,

Below: **A view of the boiler shop looking due south. The tall square building on the right is the hydraulic accumulator (K on the plan) which stored water at 2000 pounds per square inch for boiler riveting machines and flanging press. Beyond the boiler shop are the boiler smithy, forge and steel foundry.** *L.Y.R.S. Collection.*

of two of their colleagues - Mr. Heywood Bright and Mr. John Ramsbottom. Mr. Bright joined the Board on the 14th of July, 1887, and died on the 24th of March 1897. Mr. Ramsbottom joined the Board on the 23rd September, 1885; retired owing to ill health on the 28th April 1897, and died on the 20th of May, 1897. The directors desire to record their appreciation of the zeal and ability which at all times they manifested in the interests of the company."

THE ACHIEVEMENT

The reader must now surely agree that John Ramsbottom is an unjustly neglected master of mechanical engineering. In view of his progress from being born in a small house in Todmorden to dying in a large detached house in Alderley Edge, with an estate valued for probate at over £144,000, it would be easy to portray his life in the manner of a Victorian rags to riches novel, or treat it as an example of "Self-Help" in the Samuel Smiles manner.

While it would be pointless to deny that there are elements of both of these in his life, the reality is much more interesting than either of them. Many of his twenty-three patents (not forty as often stated), along with other machines which he developed, helped to transform both the weaving industry, and workshop practice in this country, and to do so irrevocably.

Ramsbottom's original mind can not only be seen in the three patented inventions detailed in the Appendix "Habits of Thought" but also in his use of wooden-framed tenders for his locomotives. As pointed out by Sir John Aspinall in his Hawkshaw Lecture to the Institution of Mechanical Engineers in 1922, wooden-framed tenders were used not just because they were cheaper, but because, in the event of a collision, the tender was designed to collapse first and save all the impact from reaching the passenger carriages. Though not mentioned by Aspinall, an additional virtue of this arrangement was that any water bursting from the tender would tend to reduce the risk of fire on the accident site.

The similarities with the modern concept of a "crumple zone" in car design are obvious, though Ramsbottom's idea might also, perhaps be called a "concertina zone". How far these expectations were realised is difficult to assess but, at a time when carriages were made almost entirely of wood, and trains had no continuous brakes, any design feature which reduced the risk of injury and death among passengers has to be applauded.

In order to understand Ramsbottom's unique contribution to railway engineering it is necessary to highlight his achievements at Crewe and Horwich.

As an engineer, administrator and disciplinarian he built up the locomotive department and Crewe Works to twice its size in ten years. By the end of 1866 the Old Works and its southern annexe was repairing 15 engines and tenders each week; constructing a new goods engine every two and a quarter working days; rebuilding 20 or more older engines and scrapping many more in a year; making 6,000 tons of iron rails a year; and undertaking most of the new workshop construction. On the basis of output per square foot, no other steam locomotive works ever equalled this feat of production.

None of this would have been possible without the use of new production methods, and quality control, on an unprecedented scale. If there had not been the qualitative shift from craft skills to Ramsbottom's batch production methods, it would have been extremely difficult, if not impossible, for the L.N.W.R. to centralise the production and repair of locomotives at Crewe. Having been pioneered at Crewe, these methods were used in other railway works worldwide to reduce costs, and improve reliability.

Not content with his achievements at Crewe, Ramsbottom started again when he was 70 with the planning and building of the new works at Horwich for the Lancashire and Yorkshire Railway, which lasted for nearly one hundred years.

Few men have had the luck and talent to make a success of one locomotive works, but the honour of making a success of two falls to just one man - John Ramsbottom.

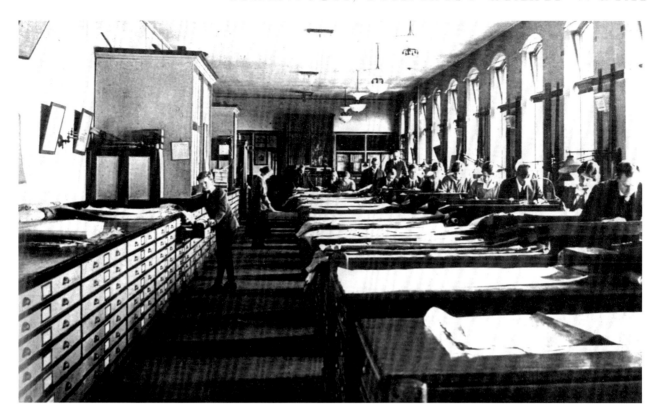

Above: The drawing office at Horwich had natural light from the left and electric uplighters. *Below:* The boiler shop was 143 yards x 37 yards and had three bays fitted with overhead cranes and hydraulic 2000 p.s.i. riveting machines. There were also pits into which boilers could be lowered vertically to a convenient working height. Rope driven quadratic stay tapping machines enabled the four sides of a firebox to be worked on at the same time. *L.Y.R.S. Collection.*

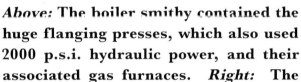

Above: The boiler smithy contained the huge flanging presses, which also used 2000 p.s.i. hydraulic power, and their associated gas furnaces. *Right:* The forge was equipped with annealing furnaces, 5 and 8 ton drop hammers, a 35 ton duplex hammer, rolling mills and a tyre rolling mill along with the necessary furnaces fed by 16 Wilson Gas producers. *Below:* The steel, iron and chair foundries had a row of Siemens-Martin acid open hearth steel melting furnaces and two small Bessemer style converters. The gas for these came from nine Wilson Gas producers. The foundries operated on two levels using the higher ground on the north side of the site. *L.Y.R.S. Collection.*

Above: The main smithy contained 40 smiths' hearths along with 11 single frame steam hammers of 8 hundredweight capacity. *Below left:* The spring smithy produced all the leaf springs for locomotives and tenders. Initially, each spring was made by a skilled spring maker but by the Edwardian period spring plate preparing machines had taken over leaving only the setting of the camber, hardening, tempering and testing to be done manually. *Below right:* The signal shop manufactured signal frames in the north side of the shop and posts and signals as seen here in the south side. *L.Y.R.S. Collection.*

Left and below: The machine shop at Horwich was 508 feet long by 111 feet wide divided into three main aisles. Down the centre of each ran a 5 ton walking jib crane and a double line of the 18 inch gauge works railway. The shop was arranged so that heavy slotting, radial drilling and planing machines were nearest to the forge and foundry. Milling machines were grouped for each activity such as cylinder work, brass work etc. The view down the centre aisle shows milling machines on the left and heavy slotters on the right. That nearest the camera is machining an inside cylinder casting. Within the machine shop was a separate fenced off tool room responsible for tool manufacture, tool sharpening and the production of jigs for the many repetitive production jobs. *L.Y.R.S. Collection.*

Left: The camera man has his back to the boiler shop to take this shot of the stores yard crane with the main stores building beyond. Just visible at the bottom left of the crane is the back of the main check lodge. The saw tooth roof of the paint shop can also be seen.

Centre: The works narrow gauge had 7½ miles of track. In this view *Dot* is seen pulling a locomotive boiler by the timber yard.

Below: Home time for the Horwich workforce as they make their way out into Chorley New Road.

L.Y.R.S. Collection.

APPENDIX ONE
JOINT REPORT ON SIZE OF ENGINES

Mems:
Joint report on size of Engines
Minutes 40 and 677

The quantity of heat which a boiler can generate is directly as the quantity of atmospheric air which can be forced through the fire, and this is the true measure of its power.

The quantity of air which can be passed through in a given time is practically limited by the area of the tubes only, (considered as flues), and is as the square of the diameter of the cylindrical part of the boiler, and inversely as the square root of the lengths of the tubes, all other things being equal.

The practice of burning Coal, and the shallow fires - together with the admission of air through the fire door, or other equivalent openings - which it necessitates, admits of a much greater quantity of work being done on a given grate surface than when coke is used, and in fire boxes of even moderate dimensions, reduces the resistance to the passage of air through the fire to an almost inappreciable quantity.

The supply of air being practically limited by the flue area, it follows that a larger fire box and grate surface - and of consequence a larger fire - means slower combustion, the temperature of the fire is lowered, the gases are consumed with greater difficulty from being immediately exposed to a large extent of cooling surface (which the fire box is, in relation to these gases) whilst the heat generated is transmitted more slowly through the thick copper than through the comparatively thin brass tubes.

The weight of the boiler is also increased by the substitution of copper for brass.

Midfeathers are objectionable, and in cases where they have been taken out, no appreciable falling off in the quantity of steam generated has been observed.

That is the best boiler, which, in proportion to its total heating surface, admits of the heated gases being passed through it with the least resistance.

Fire box surface alone cannot be taken as the measure of the power of the boiler, for if so, then No.300 S.D. ought to be upwards of three times, No.291 S.D. (Bloomer Class) nearly twice, and the G.N. New Engine more than twice the power of our new N.D. Engine, Problem, which is very far from being the case.

For the above reasons I consider that No.291 S.D. is the most powerful in the following list; the cylindrical part of the boiler is larger in diameter, and the flue area consequently greater than in any of the rest, the total heating surface is also greater whilst the grate surface is such as to offer but little resistance to the passage of the air through the fire, particularly when coal is used.

The G.N. has a larger fire box which however cannot be brought into full play, owing to the limited flue area, the boiler being only 4 feet diameter.

Both these engines would be better without midfeathers, particularly for coal burning.

The "Problem" N.D. Engine is as large in proportion to the requirements of this Division as No.291 is for the S.D. and the proportions of cylinder, stroke and driving wheel, in both, are better adapted to quick running than those of the G.N. or the Caln. Engine.

Both the "G.N." and the Caln. Engines have outside framing, which adds considerably to the weight, without increasing their power.

Engine "Problem" has been designed with reference to the limit of weight imposed by the Directors, (26 tons), but the size of the boiler can be readily increased if required.

Both "Problem" and "No.291" are the most powerful Engines, in proportion to their weight, of any in this list.

Crewe May 9th 1860

COMMENTS

This document is interesting in that it shows Ramsbottom had grasped, more firmly than some of his contemporaries, the fact that the area through the tubes is crucial in designing a free steaming boiler, as it limits the amount of air which can be drawn through the fire bed, and hence the rate of combustion.

In his first paper to the Institution of Mechanical Engineers, "On an Improved Locomotive Boiler", in 1849 he had highlighted this, and been critical of the fact that boiler heating surface had been increasing since 1842 "by enlarging the fire-box, by putting in a midfeather, and by increasing the length rather than the number of tubes" - all points which he returned to in his report to the Directors in 1860.

In more recent times the area through the tubes has been expressed as a percentage of the grate area, known as "free gas area" for short. The B.R. Standard designs all had a free gas area of over 14%, and it is worth noting that all three L.& N.W.R. designs exceed this figure.

The percentages for free gas area, based on Ramsbottom's figures, are as follows:-

Problem 14.9%; 291 Bloomer S.D. 14.8%; 300 S.D. 14.2%; New G.N.Ry. 9.6%; Caledonian Express 14.4%; South Eastern 8.8%.

How far Ramsbottom was selecting his examples in order to show the Directors that the locomotives produced at Crewe and Wolverton were among the best in the country is an open question. One hopes that the Directors were pleased with the results of this analysis.

Though not covered in his report in 1860 to the Directors, Ramsbottom had also shown in his 1849 paper that he was concerned about the fact that locomotives were being fitted with relatively smaller blast pipes than previously. He said that " . . . as the whole of the steam (after having performed its office in the cylinders) is driven in a forcible jet up the chimney for the purpose of producing the necessary draught through the fire, . . . it follows that the smaller the blast-pipe is in proportion to the total heating surface of the boiler, the greater will be the resistance to the action of the piston, and the greater the loss of power on this account."

The section dealing with the volume of "Steam Discharge per Mile" is rather a puzzle. The back pressure in the blast pipe has subsequently been proved to depend on the weight of steam issuing per unit of time (irrespective of the speed), and not the volume per mile. It is not clear, therefore, what point Ramsbottom was trying to illustrate with this heading.

One interesting point is that Ramsbottom had designed Problem to meet the weight limit set by the Directors (he actually exceeded it by 15 cwt.), but was keen to point out that a larger boiler could be fitted if required. This rebuilding did not happen until F. W. Webb was in charge.

It is also not surprising, given the views expressed on boiler design in the report to the Directors, that no locomotive of the Stephenson long-boiler type was built at Longsight or Crewe while Ramsbottom was in charge.

One of the engines used in Ramsbottom's report was this Caledonian Railway 2-2-2 with 8ft 2in diameter driving wheels designed by Benjamin Conner. *Caledonian Railway Association.*

The Problem class was the London & North Western's Northern Division engine used in the comparison. No. 291, *Prince of Wales*, is seen here at Stafford in as built condition. *L.N.W.R. Society.*

Table Showing the Comparative Proportions of Pass'r Engines on Various Railways.

Engine	Cylinder		Dia. of Driving Wheel		Steam Pressure per sq. in.	Diam. of Boiler		Tubes			Heating Surface			Grate Area		Pass. Air Area		Wheel Base		Total Weight			
	Dia.	Stroke	ft	in	Cub ft	ft	in	No.	Length ft	in	Sectional Area	Fire Box sq ft	Tubes Total sq ft	Total sq ft	sq ft	sq ft	sq ft	ft	in	Working Order tons cwt		Empty tons cwt	
Problem. L&NW R.	16	24	7	6	2502	4	0	192	10	9	1⅛	85	1013	1098	312	14.5	98	833	15	5	26	15	23	17
291 Service Class L&NW R.	16	22	7	0	2657	4	1¾	195	12	1	2⅛	165	1310	1475	404	19		900	16	10	29	2	25	8
300 L&NW R.	18	24	7	6	3166	4	3¾	303	7	0	1¾	260	972	1232	449	22		1238	16	10	31	0	25	0
Flg Express G.N. Ry.	17	22	7	0	2774	4½	0	168	10	3½	2	180	840	1060	297	213		1152	18	0		34		
Caledonian Express	18	24	8	0	2968	4	0	191	11	8	1⅞	83	1092	1180	282	136		762						
South Eastern						3	10⅜	181	10	0	2	134	927	1081	320	25.3								

APPENDIX TWO
JOHN RAMSBOTTOM'S PATENTS

YEAR	PATENT NO.	SUBJECT
1834	Nº 6644	Vertical loom and weft-fork. (With Richard Holt)
1836	Nº 6975	Roving, spinning, and doubling of fibres.
1848	Nº 12384	Railway wheels, and turntables [with thrust races]. (With William Baker)
1852	Nº 767	Metallic piston and piston rings, and hydraulic throttle valve.
1854	Nº 309	Hydraulic hoist for rolling stock.
"	Nº 408	Improvements in welding.
1855	Nº 322	Piston rings improvements.
"	Nº 1299	Safety valves, and feed water cistern.
1857	Nº 1047	Wrought iron rail chair.
1860	Nº 1527	Water trough and scoop.
"	Nº 2460	Displacement lubricator.
1863	Nº 924	Duplex steam hammer & cogging mill
1864	Nº 48	Manufacture of hoops and tyres.
1864	Nº 3073	Bessemer Converter improvements.
1865	Nº 89	Steam hammer improvements.
"	Nº 375	Hammering and rolling machinery.
"	Nº 736	Improvements to 1863, Nº 924.
"	Nº 1425	Improvements to 1864, Nº 48.
"	Nº 1975	Improvement processes for hoops and tyres.
1867	Nº 342	Supporting ingots for steam hammer.
"	Nº 386	Traverser for rolling stock.
1868	Nº 2956	Communication cord (Provisional only)
1869	Nº 820	Ventilating tunnels.
1880	Nº 1060	Trip gear for steam and gas engines.

24 Patent Applications

23 PATENTS

This list is shorter than the forty patents usually credited to Ramsbottom. Please note that there were three engineers of the name "John Ramsbottom" taking out patents in the 1850s and 1860s. The Patent Office indexes do not differentiate between the three: only the texts of the individual patents make it clear which "John Ramsbottom" is the source of the patent.

AN EXAMPLE OF A RAMSBOTTOM PATENT

RAMSBOTTOM'S LUBRICATING APPARATUS.

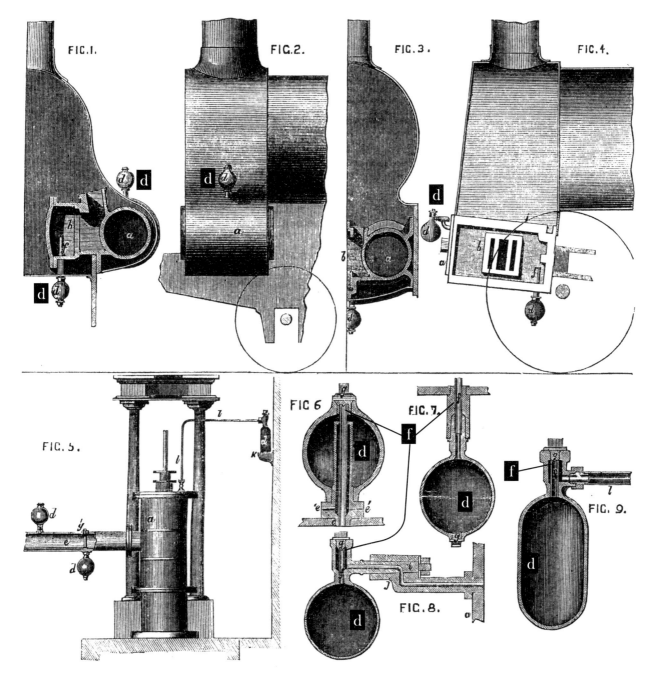

Above: **Ramsbottom's lubricator worked on the displacement principle. The vessel d in Figs. 6, 7, 8 or 9 is filled with lubricant until it is level with the upper orifice of pipe f. The lower orifice of pipe f is open to the interior of the steam pipe, chest or cylinder to be lubricated. When the engine is working, steam will rise up pipe f and on coming into contact with the cool lubricant will condense as water. It will then descend through its own weight to the bottom of vessel d thereby displacing a little lubricant through pipe f into the cylinder, where it will lubricate the piston. This process will continue as long as the engine is working or until the lubricant is all used. To replenish the vessel the water is removed and the oil refilled. *Author's Collection.***

APPENDIX THREE
PAPERS PRESENTED
TO THE I. MECH. E.

Ramsbottom presented twelve full papers to the Institution of Mechanical Engineers (I. Mech. E.) between 1849 and 1871. The full text of these can be found in the Proceedings of the Institution. They are as follows:

YEAR	SUBJECT
1849	On an Improved Locomotive Boiler
1853	Description of an Improved Coking Crane for Supplying Locomotive Tenders
1854	On an Improved Piston for Steam Engines
1855	On the Construction of Packing Rings for Pistons
1856	On an Improved Safety Valve
1857	Description of a Safety Escape Pipe for Steam Boilers
1861	Description of a Method of Supplying Water to Locomotive Tenders whilst Running
1864	On the Improved Traversing Cranes at Crewe Locomotive Works
1866	Description of an Improved Reversing Rolling Mill
1867	On an Improved Mode of Manufacture of Steel Tyres
1867	Description of a 30-ton Horizontal Duplex Hammer
1871	On the Mechanical Ventilation of the Liverpool Passenger Tunnel on the London and North Western Railway
1871	Supplementary Paper on the above

DIAGRAMS OF REVERSING ROLLING MILL - 1866

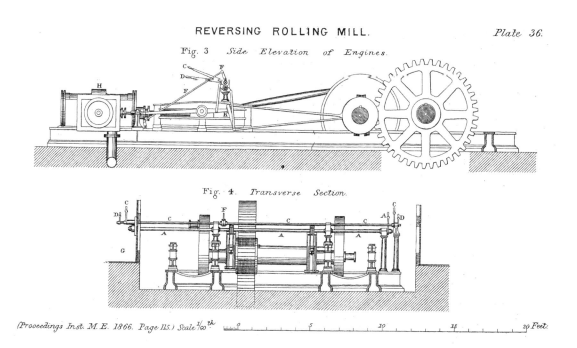

REVERSING ROLLING MILL.   Plate 36.

Fig. 3   Side   Elevation   of   Engines.

Fig. 4.   Transverse   Section.

(Proceedings Inst. M.E. 1866. Page 115.) Scale ¹/₆₀ᵗʰ   0   5   10   15   20 Feet

REVERSING ROLLING MILL.   *Plate 34.*

Fig. 1.—General Plan of Rolling Mill and Engines.

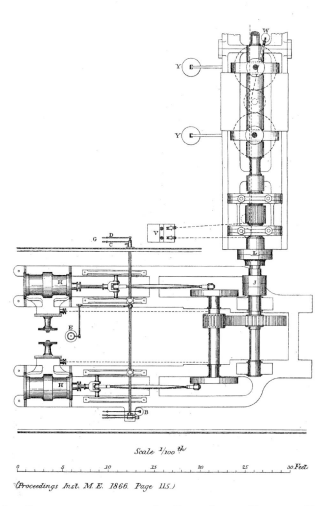

Scale ¹/₁₀₀ th

0   5   10   15   20   25   30 Feet.

(Proceedings Inst. M. E. 1866. Page 115.)

"The special point in the arrangement is that the rolls are directly driven by the engine, without the intervention of a flywheel; and the engine and rolls together are reversed each time that a heat [steel ingot] is passed through, the rolling being alternately in opposite directions." *Ramsbottom's own words.*

REVERSING ROLLING MILL.   *Plate 38*

Fig. 8.   Elevation of Roughing-Down Rolls.

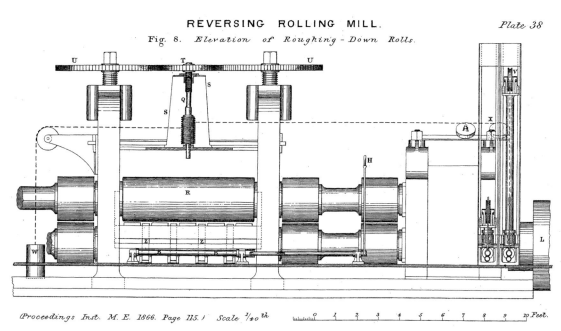

(Proceedings Inst. M. E. 1866. Page 115.)   Scale ¹/₄₀ th   0 1 2 3 4 5 6 7 8 9 10 Feet.

APPENDIX FOUR
RAMSBOTTOM'S
HABITS OF THOUGHT

I would like to draw your attention to three of the inventions which Ramsbottom patented and, more importantly, were the subject of papers he read to the Institution of Mechanical Engineers. These are the split piston ring patented in 1855, the water-trough of 1860, and the duplex steam-hammer of 1865.

These papers are invaluable because they give the background to the problem Ramsbottom faced, and the solution he came up with in his own words. In each case it will be found that he looked at the problem from an unexpected direction and came up with what, in hindsight, was an obvious solution.

SPLIT PISTON RINGS

Dealing first with the split piston-ring, it is clear that all was not well with the piston rings used on the cast-iron piston patented in 1852. By the time of Ramsbottom's patent and paper in 1855 experience had shown that it was not enough merely to fit a piston ring 10% larger than the diameter of the cylinder because the rings were wearing unevenly.

In his paper he says, "It was taken for granted that the unequal wear above referred to was owing to the pressure against the cylinder being unequal in different parts of the ring, and as the packing rings used by the writer are made of wire or drawn rods, and consequently equal in thickness, it was found impracticable to ensure this equable pressure by tapering the ring - but as this uniform pressure can be obtained by making the packing ring truly *circular in figure*, but *unequal in thickness*, it occurred to the writer, inasmuch as the rings he employs are bent and not turned, that the same end might be gained by making the ring *equal in strength* of material but *unequal in figure*, or in other words that a ring might be made of such a shape, that although uniform in cross section, it would press equally against the working surface of the cylinder all round."

"It may be possible to determine geometrically the form of ring required, but the writer preferred to solve the problem in a practical manner by the following method:- A ring was first bent truly circular in shape, and of a diameter exactly equal to that of the piston for which it was intended, the ends just touching at the joint, but without

pressure; this ring was then placed on a circular table . . . and a number of strings, say 24 in all, were attached at equal distances apart round the circumference, and passed over the same number of small pulleys which were fixed at equal distances round the edge of the table; to these strings were attached equal weights FF, which acting upon equal portions of the circumference of the circular ring brought it into the shape shown in Fig 3. The writer then conceived that if a true circle were brought into this shape, when subjected to equal radial forces acting upon equal portions of its circumference, another ring bent to the figure so obtained would conversely be brought to a truly circular shape by the application of equal forces acting in the opposite direction, that is, towards the centre instead of from it; and practice has proved that such a conclusion was correct, for a ring so bent is found to wear equally throughout, and to last much longer than those originally made circular in form."

The split piston ring is still used in almost all internal combustion engines. The rings are fitted to the piston, then squeezed in a compression tool before insertion into the cylinder where they form a gas tight seal.
L. Gardner & Son

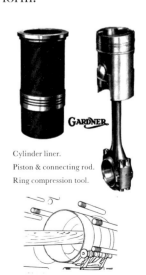

Cylinder liner.
Piston & connecting rod.
Ring compression tool.

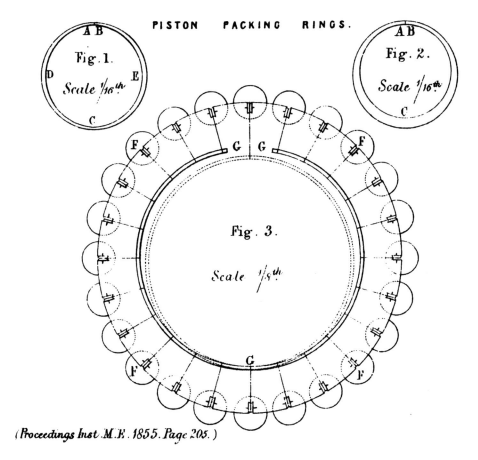

PISTON PACKING RINGS.

(Proceedings Inst. M.E. 1855. Page 205.)

The illustration above shows how Ramsbottom arranged weights to determine the correct shape of an uncompressed piston ring. The one below shows how rings were located on a steam locomotive piston. *Institution of Mechanical Engineers.*

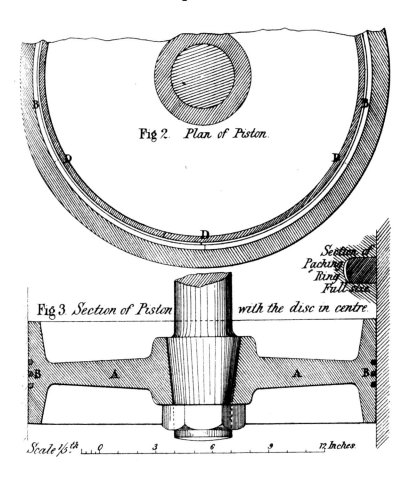

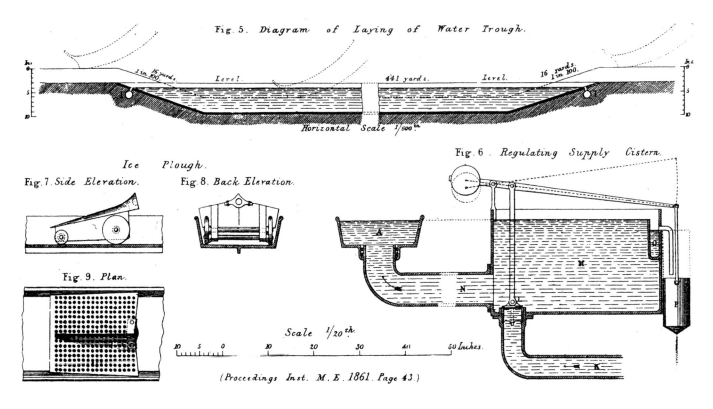

Fig. 5. *Diagram of Laying of Water Trough.*

Horizontal Scale 1/500th.

Ice Plough.

Fig. 7. *Side Elevation.*

Fig. 8. *Back Elevation.*

Fig. 6. *Regulating Supply Cistern.*

Fig. 9. *Plan.*

Scale 1/20th.

(*Proceedings Inst. M. E. 1861. Page 43.*)

WATER TROUGHS

Turning now to the water-trough, his paper of 1860 was entitled *Description of a Method of Supplying Water to Locomotive Tenders Whilst Running*, and the background information is only given about four-fifths way through. The earlier part of the paper is devoted to an extended description of the trough and the scoop, and the tests he carried out to confirm that his basic idea was correct - that the motion of a moving train through a static water supply would raise sufficient water into the tender. Several of the preliminary experiments used a stream of water moving at 15 m.p.h. to see if water could be made to flow away smoothly from the top of a tube up to $7\frac{1}{2}$ feet high.

While I am aware of statements to the effect that the idea of the water-trough came from John Bland of the drawing office, I have not, as yet, come across any direct evidence to support this, and it is contradicted by Ramsbottom's own words. I must also point out that in other papers to the Institution of Mechanical Engineers where credit was due to others, then it was given. Of course it is quite possible that he treated his staff differently from professional colleagues but, at present, evidence is lacking to prove the case either way.

Regarding the water-trough what he said was:- "The principle of action of this plan of raising water for supplying locomotive tenders occurred to the writer several years ago, and he long felt convinced that it . . . [could be used] . . . with some advantages of importance in removing difficulties that are at present experienced under certain circumstances of working the traffic. His attention was forcibly called to this on occasion of having to provide last year for the accelerated working of the Irish mail, which has now to be run through from Chester to Holyhead, a distance of $84\frac{3}{4}$ miles, without stopping, in 2 hours and 5 minutes. This necessitated an increase in the size of the tender tanks beyond the largest size previously used containing 2000 gallons; or else required the alternative of taking water half way at Conway, either by stopping the train for the purpose, or by picking up the water whilst running. A supply of 2400 gallons is found requisite for this journey in rough weather; and although 1800 to 1900 gallons only are consumed in fair weather, it is necessary to be always provided for the larger supply, on account of the very exposed condition of the greater portion of the line, which causes the train to be liable to great increase of resistance from the high winds frequently encountered. An increase of the tender tanks beyond the present size of 2000 gallons would have involved an objectionable increase of weight in construction, and alteration in the standard sizes of wheels and axles &c. for tenders; and would have also caused a waste of locomotive power in dragging the extra load along the line. By this plan of picking up 1000 gallons of water at the half way point near Conway, where the water trough is fixed, the necessity for a tender larger than the previous size of 1500 gallons is avoided, effecting a reduction in load equivalent to another carriage of the train."

As an aside, I would like to point out that evaporating 2400 gallons of water in 2 hours 5 minutes gives an average evaporation rate of 11,520 lbs. per hour, or approximately 795 lbs. of steam per sq.ft. of grate area, taking the grate as 14.5 sq.ft. The Ramsbottom boiler was therefore a very effective steam producer, though its efficiency is unknown. (A Stanier "Duchess" Pacific, some seventy five years later, would have to be producing steam at a rate of 39,750 lbs. per hour to equal this.)

Opposite page: **Ramsbottom's diagrams show how the water trough would be laid out and kept supplied with water. He also designed an ice plough to keep the trough free of ice in winter.** *Institution of Mechanical Engineers.*

Below: **The arrangement of the water scoop and its operating mechanism can be seen in both the drawing and the model tender with its cut out side illustrating the flange to which the delivery pipe would be attached.** *Photo Courtesy of N.R.M.*

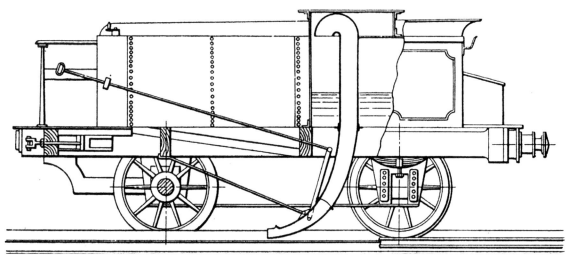

Fig. 1. *Side Elevation and Longitudinal Section of 30 ton Horizontal Duplex Hammer.*

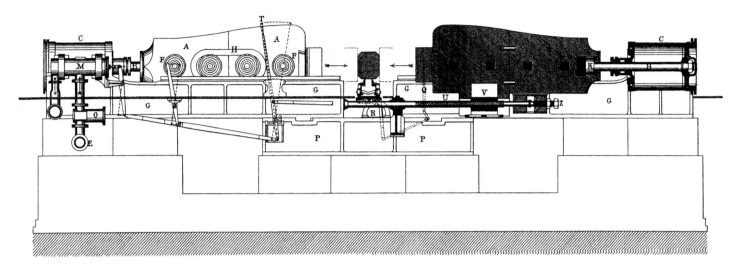

(Proceedings Inst. M. E. 1867. Page 218.)

Scale 1/80 th

DUPLEX STEAM HAMMER

My third example is the duplex steam hammer, explained in Ramsbottom's own words. "The hammer described in this paper arose out of the writer's belief that it was necessary to provide some means more powerful than any before used in England, and at the same time convenient and handy, for the forging of steel in large masses. His attention was first drawn to this question when he was engaged in laying out the Bessemer Steel Works of the London and North Western Railway at Crewe. The first intention was to put down a 30 ton vertical hammer of the ordinary kind; but as this would have required an anvil of 300 tons, the practical difficulty and cost of dealing with so large a mass suggested to the writer that the principle of action and reaction might afford a solution to the problem. Hence arose the conception of two hammers acting in opposite directions; and as a matter of convenience it seemed better to lay them on their side and cause them to operate horizontally upon a bloom placed between them. As this idea grew into form it appeared to present advantages both in economy and convenience sufficiently important to warrant the construction of an experimental hammer of 10 tons. This when brought into operation proved to possess the advantages expected; and in consequence the writer designed and laid down the 30 ton hammer which forms the subject of the present paper."

Unlike the 10 ton hammer which had only one vertical steam cylinder, and used connecting rods from the cylinder to draw the tups together simultaneously, the 30 ton hammer had two cylinders each 38" by 42" stroke, and fitted with piston valves. Each tup was mounted on eight wheels, running on steel rails. In order to ensure the tups moving simultaneously, and striking the bloom at exactly the same instant, each tup was connected through a brass nut to a long screw shaft with right and left hand threads carried under the centre line of the hammer.

The 30 ton hammer was capable of converting a crank-axle ingot from its cast size of 20" x 24" and 3' 5" long to a slab $11\frac{3}{4}$" x $21\frac{1}{2}$" and 5' 10" long using 312 blows of the hammer. Of these the main work was carried out by 228 blows delivered at a rate of up to 48 per minute, the process taking about 25 minutes.

The chief advantages of the duplex hammer can be summarised as being:-

- It requires no anvil because the whole moving force of each hammer tup is balanced by the one opposed to it. Hence the cost of laying down and of occasionally lifting an anvil is avoided. A comparatively shallow foundation is required, a matter of great importance where drainage is difficult. It is also possible to instal a duplex hammer in a building that could not take the height of a vertical hammer of the same power.

- The blows, being in opposite directions, counteract each other, hence no vibration is produced, and consequently no damage is done to the surrounding buildings and machinery.

- In working, it will be seen that the scale can fall away quite freely from the bloom, and also that there is great ease of manipulation, and consequent accuracy, in the forging of large masses.

- Due to the short stroke used it is possible to achieve great rapidity of action, up to 48 blows per minute. This is more than could be achieved by a 5 ton vertical hammer supplied with steam from the same boiler.

- Due to the rapid action that can be achieved it is possible to finish the forging of even long bars in a single heat, thereby preventing the waste of skinning the iron over with a coat of oxide by a second heating. In this way a great deal of time and skilled labour is saved, as well as the fuel required for a second heat.

- The hammer is therefore an economical instrument in first cost, cost of operation, and cost of maintenance.

I have dealt with the duplex hammer at greater length largely because it ceased to be used at Crewe more than one hundred years ago, and is therefore less familiar than the other two examples.

Further developments which Ramsbottom outlined, but which did not happen at Crewe, were for the duplex hammer to be used for the manufacture of gun barrels and other long and heavy articles, and in conjunction with a vertical hammer for forgings requiring two kinds of treatment. Given all these advantages I find it surprising that the idea was not used widely.

Opposite page and below: **The construction and operation of Ramsbottom's duplex hammer can be seen in the drawings taken from the *Proceedings of the Institution of Mechanical Engineers* for 1867.**

HORIZONTAL DUPLEX HAMMER. *Plate 65.*

Fig. 2. *Plan and Sectional Plan of* **30** *ton Horizontal Duplex Hammer.*

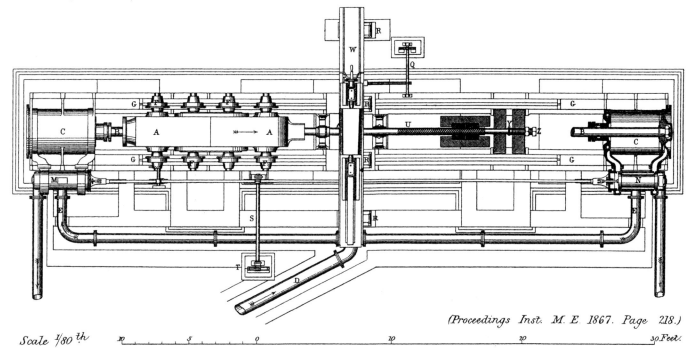

(Proceedings Inst. M. E. 1867. Page 218.)

Scale 1/80th

APPENDIX FIVE
THE "RAMSBOTTOM" IRONCLADS

In 1875 Ramsbottom was called on by the ever abrasive Sir Edward Watkin, by now the Chairman of the South Eastern Railway, to provide a report on the works and locomotives of the company. This was quite an extreme step for Watkin to take as he was going over the head of the Locomotive Superintendent, James Cudworth, who had held that position for many years and was himself a member of the Institution of Mechanical Engineers. Relations between Watkin and Cudworth appear to have been poor, and they deteriorated further in the summer of 1875 with the late running of Dover boat trains.

It is not clear when Watkin made his first approach to Ramsbottom but, given the rapid pace at which events moved, it is obvious that discussions must have been going on for some time previously. The first the Directors of the S.E.R. knew was on 29 September 1875 when Watkin told them that Ramsbottom had accepted a commission to inspect the line and present a written report within 15 days.

On 2 October Ramsbottom paid a visit to the railway. He was met at London Bridge by Cudworth and they then proceeded to Ashford works by way of Bricklayer's Arms depot and Tonbridge. After visiting the works they went to Dover and returned to London by a fast train. (What does one say, by way of conversation, to a founder member and past President of the Institution of Mechanical Engineers who is apparently in league with the Chairman of the Board in wanting you out of your job?)

In his report Ramsbottom was very complimentary about Cudworth's management, saying: "All trains ran to schedule, and I was greatly impressed by the mechanical order and cleanliness of all the engines and carriages observed, as well as the manner of the various grades of railwayman. The works at Ashford were well organized and equipped." (It is worth noting that there would have been very little time to put on a special effort at Ashford.)

Ramsbottom's report agreed that more powerful engines were needed. "Twenty express passenger engines with conventional coal-burning fireboxes [are required] capable of working 170 ton trains at 50 miles an hour up gradients of 1 in 50. They should be 2-4-0s with inside frames, 17-inch cylinders, 4 ft. 2 in. diameter boilers and a weight of 31 tons." On the basis of what can only be called a cursory visit, Ramsbottom had drawn up a fairly detailed specification.

This report was received on 6 October and presented to the Board the following day. The Board decided to reserve judgement to a later meeting on 18 November. At this meeting Cudworth was authorised to seek tenders for twenty locomotives to be built to the drawings that Ramsbottom had furnished, in time for the summer services the following year.

At a meeting held on 2 December ten tenders were received and read out. Only Sharp Stewart and Co., and the Avonside Engine Company were able to meet the need to provide locomotives for the summer of 1876, and each was given an order for ten engines, with the former providing all the drawings. The Sharp Stewart locomotives cost £2,385 each and the Avonside engines £2,350 each, a grand total of £47,350.

The Sharp Stewart locomotives were delivered between July and September 1876, the Avonside locos between September and December.

This whole episode raises many questions, to which there appear to be few answers. Given the hundreds of drawings needed for the construction of any steam locomotive, and the fact that he did not himself have an office in Manchester in the 1870s, Ramsbottom must have received considerable assistance from the drawing office of one of the contract locomotive builders in the city, or from the Gorton works of the Manchester, Sheffield, and Lincolnshire Railway – also chaired by Watkin. The phrase "conflict of interest" comes to mind but, leaving that to one side (which they did – and how!), it would be interesting to know which drawing office was involved. Somebody must have been really cracking on even to copy a set of drawings in six weeks, at a time when all copying was manual. The only way Ramsbottom could have avoided any conflict of interest would have been by using the drawing office of his Goodfellow relations in Hyde, who had no experience of building railway engines.

Opposite page: **Sharp Stewart built locomotive No.266 is seen here painted in photographic grey livery when new.** *South Eastern & Chatham Railway Society*

Below: **Sister engine No.267 in original condition with crew posed on footplate.** *South Eastern & Chatham Railway Society.*

Almost from the moment the locomotives started arriving it became clear that they were no better than Cudworth's own and they were quickly drafted on to secondary services where they remained until they were withdrawn some twenty to thirty years later. After spending £47,350 on twenty locomotives it seems strange, to put it mildly, that the S.E.R. did not have some frank discussions with the builders and Ramsbottom about improving their performance. It is a complete mystery why the locomotives could not meet the specification Ramsbottom himself had laid down.

While the dimensions of the Ironclads were similar to Webb's Precedent class which had appeared from Crewe in 1874, there were many small differences of no more than three inches, including wheel sizes. This means that Crewe did not merely supply drawings to be used by another builder. As far as steaming is concerned, the most significant difference was that of the grate area, which was only 15.25 sq. ft. as compared to the 17.1 sq. ft. of the Precedent class. Unfortunately the Ironclads never achieved as good a reputation as the Precedents even after new boilers were fitted, starting in 1888.

As a footnote to this, I should like to draw your attention to a 2-4-0 built by Sharp Stewart and Co. for the Paris Exhibition of 1878, and described in detail in D.K.Clark's *The Steam Engine*. Clark says "Several engines of the same type were previously constructed for the South-Eastern Railway", which is not quite accurate. The dimensions of this engine are very close to those of the Ironclads, except that the grate area was 17.75 sq. ft., the cylinders were 18" diameter, and boiler pressure was 140 p.s.i. This locomotive was sold to the Paris Orleans Railway after the Exhibition, but nothing is known of it thereafter.

Below: **Engine No.273 was one of the Avonside built batch and was caught by the photographer at Bricklayers Arms about 1885, still in original condition.** *South Eastern & Chatham Railway Society.*

Above and below: **From 1888 the Ironclads were rebuilt with new domeless boilers. The makers plate was removed at the same time and the number plate moved to the cab splasher. The photographs on this page show Nos.269 and 272 in rebuilt condition.** ***South Eastern & Chatham Railway Society.***

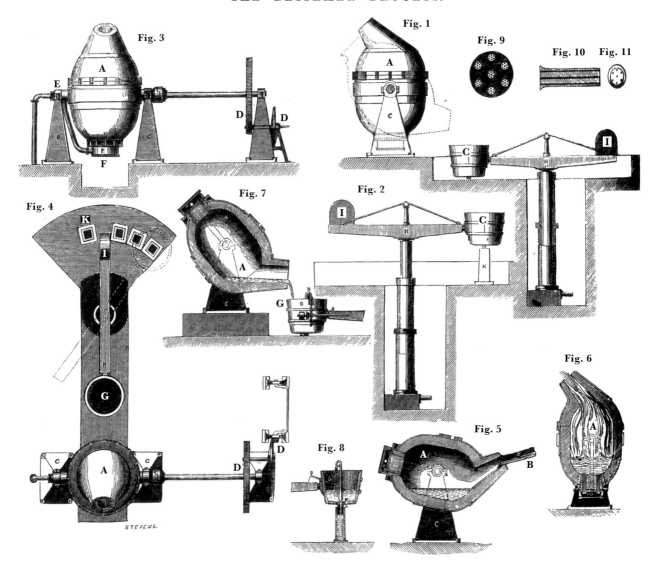

APPENDIX SIX
THE BESSEMER PROCESS

The Bessemer converter was last used to produce steel in Workington in 1974, and no-one under the age of about fifty can have seen, and experienced, one in regular use. Because this process is now a dead technology, and because it was so important when it came into use in the 1860s, a short explanation of the process is needed to convey some idea of the initial impact of Bessemer steel on the world of engineering.

An article from *The Engineer* in 1862 gives a description of the converter at John Brown and Co.'s Atlas Works in Sheffield, and some useful period drawings. These are entirely consistent with the photographs of the Bessemer steel plant at Crewe, and help one to understand it.

The core of the process is the Bessemer converter (A in Figs. 1 and 3). This rests on bearings E, and can be turned to the various positions needed through the gearing DD. Compressed air from a blowing engine is brought, at about 14 p.s.i., up the pipe to the left of the converter in Fig. 3, through one of the bearings, to the tuyere box (F, and Fig. 9). There are seven tuyeres in the box. These are made of fireclay, have seven holes each, and are seen in Figs. 10 and 11.

Starting from cold, the first stage is to heat the converter. This is done by putting burning coke in it and blowing air through the tuyeres. When it has been sufficiently heated, the converter is turned upside down for the coke to fall out, and it is then put in a horizontal position (see Fig. 5).

This allows molten iron from a blast furnace to run into the converter through the spout B. The compressed air is then blown through the tuyeres, and the converter swung into an upright position - all this while it contains up to ten tons of molten iron (see Fig. 6). (The air has to be turned on first or else the molten iron would fall back through the tuyeres when the converter is swung upright.)

The sparks now begin to fly (quite literally) as the impurities in the iron - silicon, manganese, and carbon - are oxidised in succession over a period of some minutes. According to *The Engineer*: "The carbon is now burnt off so rapidly as to produce a series of harmless explosions, throwing out the fluid slag in great quantities; while the combustion of the gases is so perfect that a voluminous white flame rushes from the mouth of the vessel, illuminating the whole building, and indicating to the practised eye the precise condition of the metal inside."

After the flames from the converter have died down, steel of the desired quality is achieved by adding back a small quantity of a special cast iron containing carbon and manganese called "spiegeleisen". In order to ensure this is fully mixed in there is a further burst of air for a few seconds through the tuyeres.

The converter is then turned nearly upside down (see Fig. 7) and the molten steel is poured into the casting ladle G. This ladle is carried by the hydraulic crane H (I is a balance weight). The crane is then raised by water pressure, and turned round roughly 180 degrees (see Figs. 2 and 4) so that the steel can be poured into the ingot moulds K. There is a plug in the bottom of the ladle to draw off the steel, so that no impurities are carried into the castings (see Fig. 8).

As *The Engineer* put it: "By this process from 1 to 10 tons of crude iron may be converted into cast steel in 30 minutes, without employing any fuel except that required for melting the pig iron and for the preliminary heating of the converting vessel, the process being effected entirely without

Below: **One of the Bessemer converters in use at Crewe works in 1894. It lasted in the same condition until 1907.** *Edward Talbot Collection.*

manipulation" [unlike wrought iron]. From being a relatively scarce and expensive metal Bessemer made steel cheap - about one fifth of its former price. With the addition of the open hearth method introduced a few years later it became commonplace - so commonplace that it is now hard to realise how the strength of steel (as compared to wrought iron) made other developments possible. Obviously, high pressure locomotive and stationary boilers would not have been possible without steel, nor would the Forth Bridge, and even in 1865 it was said that steel plates on hulls were five-eigths the thickness of iron ones.

Given the "harmless explosions, throwing out the fluid slag" it is interesting to note that the Bessemer converter went out of use at almost the same time as the Health and Safety Executive came into existence. This was extremely convenient, if nothing else.

The last Bessemer converter from Workington is now preserved at the Kelham Island Museum of the Sheffield Industrial Museums Trust, and is well worth a visit.

Below: **In 1864 Ramsbottom patented this improved method of heating the compressed air before it passed into the converter. The area of the pipe was doubled to allow pre-heated spheres to be inserted on support rails in the pipe immediately before the air passed through it. At the end of each batch the spheres were run or blown out of the pipe into a box and taken off to be re-heated as required. A carburettor was also included which mixed one part of hydrogen or other gas to thirty parts of air. It was claimed that his eliminated sulphur and phosphorus thereby increasing the range of irons that could be converted using the Bessemer process.** ***Illustrated London News.***

RAMSBOTTOM'S MANUFACTURE OF STEEL AND IRON.

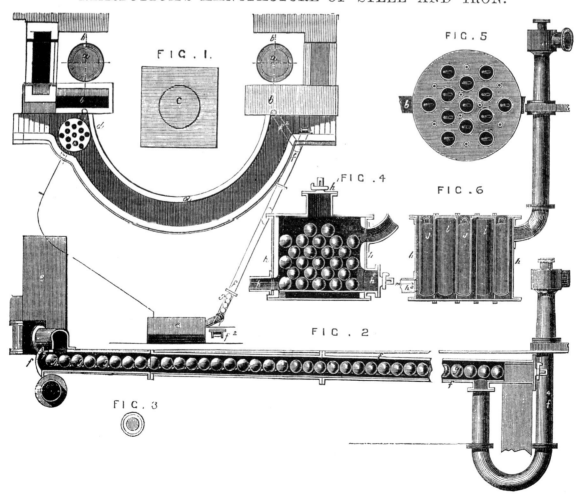

APPENDIX SEVEN
BAPTISM AT TODMORDEN
26th JUNE 1837

BAPTISED
AT ST. MARY'S TODMORDEN
26th JUNE 1837

Maria Holt (b.1795)

Susan Holt (b.1798)

Children of John and Sarah Holt (Joiner)

Hannah Ramsbotham (b.1807)

John Ramsbotham (b.1814)

Mary Ramsbotham (b.1816)

Jane Ramsbotham (b.1818)

Ann Ramsbotham (b.1820)

Note
The Ramsbotham spelling is a verbatim copy from the original record.

Children of Henry and Sarah Ramsbottom (Manufacturer)

John Holt (b.1821)

Sarah Holt (b.1823)

Francis Holt (b.1825)

Maria Holt (b.1827)

Thomas Holt (b.1829)

Charles Holt (b.1831)

Hannah Holt (b.1833)

Richard Holt (b.1835)

Children of John and Mary Ann Holt (Joiner)

St. Mary's Church, Todmorden in the 1860s.
Courtesy Roger Birch.

APPENDIX EIGHT
WILLIAM HENRY RAMSBOTTOM

As he is the only member of John Ramsbottom's two families whose portrait can be provided, some information would appear to be appropriate.

He was born on 28 February 1852 at the house his parents rented in Belle Vue Place, Kirkmanshulme Lane, Newton, which was only a short distance from the shed. (This is now part of Longsight.) Mary Ramsbottom was the person who informed the Registrar on 10 April.

The 1861 Census shows that he was attending a private boarding school in Ashton-under-Lyne run by William Sunderland J.P. Besides Sunderland and his family, there were four tutors and thirty-nine boys at the school. Interestingly, two of the boys appear to have been the children of Benjamin Goodfellow, by that time

Ramsbottom's father-in-law.

He completed his schooling at Manchester Grammar School and then went to Owens College in 1868.

He practiced as a solicitor from 1877 - 1880 before deciding to enter the Church of England as a clergyman. He was ordained to a curacy in Leesfield, Ashton-under-Lyne by the Bishop of Manchester in 1880, staying there till 1882. (What his Quaker grandfather in Barnsley had to say about this is not recorded.) In the 1881 Census he was recorded as married to Charlotte (from Huddersfield) with no children, while in 1901 he was married to Annie (from Preston), and with three children aged 8, 6, and 5.

The following information has been culled from Crockford's Clerical Directory:-

1881
Author of "Hymns for Harvest Festivals."

1882-1884
Curate of Ashton-on-Ribble, Lancs., Dio. of Manchester.

1884-1889
Perpetual Curate of Woodplumpton, Preston, Dio. of Manchester.

1889
St. Paul's Mission House, Grahamstown, Cape Colony, South Africa.

1890-1891
Vicar of Richmond with Hopetown, and Priest in Charge of De Aar Junction,
Dio. of Grahamstown.

1891-1898
Rector of Christ Church, Colesburg, Cape Colony, Dio. of Grahamstown.

1898-1899
Vicar of Chapel-le-Dale (or Ingleton Fells), Yorks., Dio. of Ripon.

1899-1911
Vicar of St. Margaret's, Bentham, Lancaster, Dio. of Ripon.

1911-1913
Rector of Shelton and Newton Bromswold, Northants., Dio. of Ely.

1913-1921
Vicar of Lacock, Chippenham, Wilts., Dio. of Bristol.

1927 (last entry)
35 Sivewright St., Krugersdorp, Transvaal. (Dio. of Johannesburg.)

St. Margaret's Church, Bentham in 1920.
Courtesy Arthur Bateson

A new chancel and transept were added to the church during Ramsbottom's time, the foundation stone being laid on 23rd July 1901. Consecration by the Bishop of Ripon took place in June 1902. *Details courtesy of Sue Adams, Church Warden.*

APPENDIX NINE
A RAMSBOTTOM CHRONOLOGY

Above: **Harewood Lodge, Broadbottom, was Ramsbottom's home from 1871 until circa 1879.** *Author's Collection.*

Entries in this chronology refer to John Ramsbottom unless other individuals are named.

1805
Establishment of "The Steam Factory", the first steam powered cotton spinning mill in Todmorden.

1807
Birth of elder sister Hannah Ramsbottom.

1814
11th September. John Ramsbottom born at a house in Salford, Todmorden, probably in the room in which his obituary in the *Todmorden Advertiser* was penned.

1816
Birth of sister Mary Ramsbottom.

1818
Birth of sister Jane Ramsbottom.

1820
Birth of sister Ann(e) Ramsbottom.

1828
Death of grandfather, John Ramsbottom.

1830
15th September. According to Nock, he sees the opening of the Liverpool and Manchester Rly.

1834
12th July. Takes out first patent for vertical loom and weft-fork, in conjunction with (uncle) Richard Holt, ironfounder.

1836
6th January. Takes out second patent for roving, spinning and doubling of fibres.

1837

26th June. John Ramsbottom baptised along with the other Ramsbottom children (not including elder brother George, date of birth unknown), and Holts of two generations.

1839

May. References given by local manufacturers prior to his taking up employment with Sharp, Roberts, and Co. in Manchester.

1842

16th May. Applies for position with Manchester and Birmingham Railway at Longsight.

1847

Founder member of the Institution of Mechanical Engineers.

1848

21st December. Takes out third patent for railway wheels and turntables, in conjunction with William Baker (later first in house Chief Civil Engineer of L.N.W.R.)

1851

29th April. Marriage of John Ramsbottom and Mary Peckett, at Barnsley in the Parish of Silkstone.

1852

28th Feb. Birth of first son, William Henry Ramsbottom at Belle Vue Place, near Longsight works.
16th November. Patent for piston and piston rings.

1854

9th February. Patent for hydraulic hoist for rolling stock.
21st February. Patent for improvements in welding.

1855

12th February. Patent for improved piston rings.
7th June. Patent for safety valves and water feed cistern.

1856

Put in charge of rail rolling mill at Crewe.

1857

13th April. Patent for wrought iron rail chair.
1st August. Takes charge at Crewe of combined Northern and North Eastern Divisions.
7th August. Death of wife Mary Ramsbottom (nee Peckett) at Belle Vue Place, Kirkmanshulme, Newton.
1st September. Death of his mother Sarah Ramsbottom.

1859

12th April. Marriage of John Ramsbottom and Mary Ann(e) Goodfellow in Stockport Parish Church.
13th April. Death of his father Henry Ramsbottom.

1860

26th April. Birth of John Goodfellow Ramsbottom (1st son, 2nd marriage) at Chester Place, Crewe.
23rd June. Patent for water trough and scoop.
10th October. Patent for displacement lubricator.

1861

Last quarter. Birth of first daughter Margaret Holt Ramsbottom.

1862

1st April. Becomes Locomotive Superintendent of L.N.W.R., at Crewe.

1863

13th April. Patent for duplex steam hammer and cogging mill.

27th June. Birth of second daughter Jane Ramsbottom at Chester Place, Crewe.

1864

7th January. Patent for hoops and tyres.

12th December. Patent for Bessemer Converter improvements.

1865

11th January. Patent for improvements to steam hammer.

10th February. Patent for hammering and metal rolling machinery.

16th March. Patent for improvements to steam hammer and cogging mill.

27th March. Birth of third daughter Mary Edith Ramsbottom at Chester Place, Crewe.

25th May. Patent for improved processes for manufacture of hoops and tyres.

31st July. Patent for ingots for hoops and tyres.

1866

26th January. Visit by Prince of Wales to L.N.W.R. Works at Crewe.

7th March. Death of first daughter Margaret Holt Ramsbottom, aged 4.

10th April. Ramsbottom elected a member of the Institution of Civil Engineers.

July. Visit of Institution of Mechanical Engineers to Crewe Works.

1867

7th February. Patent for supporting ingots for steam hammer.

12th February. Patent for traverser for rolling stock.

1868

6th January. Birth of George Holt Ramsbottom (2nd son, 2nd marriage) at Chester Place, Crewe.

26th September. Patent for communication cord (provisional).

1869

18th March. Patent for ventilating tunnels.

1871

31st August. Retires from L.N.W.R., ostensibly on grounds of ill health.

1873

Establishes Ramsbottom Scholarship.

Ramsbottom Testimonial from L.N.W.R. on display at Vienna Exhibition.

1874

20th November. Birth of fourth daughter Eliza Ramsbottom at Harewood Lodge, Mottram.

1876

Death of Charles Beyer at Llantysilio (North Wales). Ramsbottom is one of three executors.

1877

William Henry Ramsbottom starts practising as a solicitor.

1878

29th May. Birth of fifth daughter Hannah Mary Ramsbottom at Harewood Lodge, Mottram.

ca.1879

Moves to Fern Hill, Alderley Edge.

1880

11th March. Takes out twenty-third patent - for trip gear for stationary engines.

William Henry Ramsbottom ordained by Bishop of Manchester to a curacy in Ashton-under-Lyne.

1882

December. Death of fourth daughter Eliza Ramsbottom.

1883

Appointed as consultant to L.&Y. Railway on new locomotive works.

1885

Appointed a director of L.&Y. Railway. Becomes a director of Beyer, Peacock & Co.

1888

Awarded honorary degree by University of Dublin.

1889

11th July. Marriage of second daughter Jane Ramsbottom to Matthew Paul, at Alderley Edge Parish Church.

1890

7th May. Birth of grandson Andrew John Ramsbottom Paul in Scotland.

1894

Last appearance at the Summer Meeting of the Institution of Mechanical Engineers, in Manchester.

John Goodfellow Ramsbottom, now Secretary of Beyer, Peacock and Company, becomes an Associate Member of the Institution of Mechanical Engineers.

1895

4th April. Birth of grand-daughter Agnes Marianne Paul in Scotland.

1897

28th April. Resigns directorship of L.&Y.R. on health grounds.

20th May. Death of John Ramsbottom at his house Fern Hill, Alderley Edge.

1902

John Goodfellow Ramsbottom emigrates to the U.S.A. arriving in Boston, Mass., on the *Laconia* on 27th November.

1918

5th September. Marriage of fifth daughter Hannah Mary Ramsbottom to Ernest William Hendy at Alderley Edge Parish Church.

1921

5th January. Death of widow Mary Ann Ramsbottom. at Highfield, Trafford Rd., Alderley Edge.

1922

26th August. Death of son (1st son, 2nd marriage) John Goodfellow Ramsbottom, in Boston, Mass.

1927

Death of first son Rev. William Henry Ramsbottom in South Africa.

1931

13th June. Death of son George Holt Ramsbottom (2nd son, 2nd marriage) at Highfield, Trafford Rd., Alderley Edge.

1948

7th February. Death of second daughter Jane Paul (nee Ramsbottom) M.B.E. at Kilcreggan.

1951

24th July. Death of third daughter Mary Edith Ramsbottom at Mount Royal Nursing Home, Minehead, Somerset.

1963

13th October. Death of grandson Andrew John Ramsbottom Paul at Carluke, Lanarkshire.

1971

15th July. Death of fifth daughter Hannah Mary (Mrs.Hendy) at Newold Cottage, Wootton Courtenay, Somerset, aged 93.

14th December. Death of grand-daughter Agnes Marianne Paul in Helensburgh, Scotland.

2003

19th July. Unveiling of plaque commemorating John Ramsbottom at Todmorden station with representatives of both the L.&Y.R. and L.N.W.R. Societies present.

It is worth noting that none of Ramsbottom's sons lived to the age of 82, though three of his daughters exceeded that. I wonder how far the atmospheric pollution arising from the vast expansion of Manchester, and of Crewe works, damaged his children's health and reduced their life expectancy.

Above: **Fern Hill, Alderley Edge, was Ramsbottom's home from circa 1879 until his death in 1897.** *Peter Sperring.*

Right: **The author, right, with The L.&Y.R. Society chairman, Ron Tinker, at the Todmorden station unveiling ceremony of the plaque commemorating John Ramsbottom.**
Noel Coates.

BIBLIOGRAPHY

The Engineer
Engineering
The English Mechanic
The Manchester Guardian
Todmorden Advertiser

Proceedings of the Institution of Mechanical Engineers 1847 - 1897.

Proceedings of the Institution of Civil Engineers 1897.

Catalogue of *The Art Treasures of the United Kingdom 1857.*

Encyclopaedia Britannica *(11th edition 1910) Articles; Crewe; Iron and Steel.*

Ahrons, E.L. *The British Steam Locomotive 1825-1925*; Bracken Books, 1987.

Atkinson, Norman. *Sir Joseph Whitworth*; Sutton Publishing Ltd., 1996.

Baines, Edward. *History, Directory, and Gazetteer of the County Palatine of Lancaster*;
    Wm. Wales, & Co, Liverpool, 1825.

Bulleid, H.A.V. *The Aspinall Era*; Ian Allan, 1977.

Chacksfield, J.E. *F.W. Webb*; Oakwood Press, 2007.

Clark, D.K. *The Steam Engine*; Blackie & Sons, 1890.

Clark, D.K. *A Manual of Rules, Tables and Data for Mechanical Engineers;* Blackie & Sons; 6th Edn., 1891.

Drummond, Diane. *Crewe: Railway Town, Company and People 1840-1914*; Scolar Press, 1995.

Ellis, C. Hamilton. *Some Classic Locomotives*; Allen & Unwin, 1949.

Hambleton, F.C. *John Ramsbottom, the Father of the Modern Locomotive*;
Stephenson Locomotive Society, 1937.

[Head, F.B.] *Stokers and Pokers*; John Murray, 1849.

Hewison, C.H. *Locomotive Boiler Explosions*; David & Charles, reprinted 2003.

Hills, Richard L. *The Life and Inventions of Richard Roberts 1789-1864;*
    Landmark Publishing 2002.

Hodgkins, David. *The Second Railway King, The Life and Times of Sir Edward Watkin*;
    Merton Priory Press, 2002.

Lowe, James W. *British Steam Locomotive Builders*; TEE Publishing, 1975.

Marshall, John. *Lancashire and Yorkshire Railway*; volume 2, David & Charles, 1970.

Neele, George P. *Railway Reminiscences*; reprinted, E.P. Publishing Ltd., 1974.

Nock O.S. *The Locomotive Engineers*; Batsford, 1955.

Nock O.S. *Premier Line*; Ian Allan, 1952.

Nock O.S. *The Lancashire and Yorkshire Railway*; Ian Allan, 1969.

Reed, Brian. *Crewe Locomotive Works and its Men*; David & Charles, 1982.

Robertson, Leslie S. *Narrow Gauge Railways – Two Feet and Under*; Plateway Press, 1988.

Savage, Mrs. E.M. *The Development of Todmorden 1700 to 1896*; Todmorden Antiquarian Society, 1987.

Smithers, Mark. *18 Inch Gauge Steam Railways*; Oxford Publishing Co., 1993.

Talbot E. and Taylor C. *Crewe Works Narrow Gauge System*; L. & N.W.R. Society, 2nd Edition 2005.

Thompson, Joseph. *The Owens College, Its Foundation and Growth*; J.E. Cornish Manchester 1886.

Ure, Andrew. *Dictionary of Arts, Manufactures, and Mines*; Longman, 1839.

JOHN RAMSBOTTOM C.E.

PRESENTED TO M^{RS} RAMSBOTTOM, ON HER HUSBAND'S RETIREMENT FROM THE
SERVICE OF THE LONDON AND NORTH WESTERN RAILWAY COMPANY,
BY THE OFFICERS AND WORKMEN EMPLOYED IN THE
LOCOMOTIVE DEPARTMENT UNDER HIS SUPERINTENDENCE. MAY, 1872.

BEQUEATHED TO THE INSTITUTION OF MECHANICAL ENGINEERS.
JOHN RAMSBOTTOM, (PRESIDENT 1870-71)
BY M^{RS} RAMSBOTTOM. OCTOBER, 1921.

Photographed by Roger Mellor, courtesy Institution of Mechanical Engineers.